Coastal and marine environmental site guide

Martin Budd

Siân John

Jonathan Simm

Mark Wilkinson

sharing knowledge
■
building best practice

CIRIA
6 Storey's Gate
Westminster
London SW1P 3AU
Telephone 020 7222 8891
Fax 020 7222 1708
Email enquiries@ciria.org.uk
Web www.ciria.org.uk

Summary

This environmental site guide provides practical advice for front-line supervisors, managers and engineers working in the coastal and marine environment on how to control impacts potentially arising from construction works. The guide has four chapters:

- Introduction
- The construction site
- Environmental issues
- Construction processes.

It is intended to be a reference book, a user-friendly guide and a training aid. This report has a companion pocket book (C590), that presents key advice on operating in the coastal and marine environment (available separately in packs of 10).

This guide reinforces and builds upon the principles relating to the control of environmental impacts arising from construction practices developed in the CIRIA *Environmental good practice on site* handbook (C502) and in other CIRIA publications.

Coastal and marine environmental site guide
Construction Industry Research and Information Association

CIRIA C584   © CIRIA 2003   ISBN 086017 584 7

Keywords: coastal and marine, construction management, environmental good practice, materials, piling, pollution prevention, recycling and reclaimed materials, regulation, site management, sustainable construction, water quality		
Reader Interest	**Classification**	
Contractors, site workers, site managers, engineers, supervisors, architects, consultants, designers and regulators	Availability: Content: Status: Users:	Unrestricted Advice/Guidance Committee guided Construction professionals and managers

Acknowledgements

This is the project report for CIRIA Research Project RP646 *Coastal and marine environmental site guide.*

The report was prepared by Posford Haskoning Ltd with support from HR Wallingford Ltd. The principal contributors from Posford Haskoning (Environment) were Martin Budd, Siân John and Mark Wilkinson, and from HR Wallingford, Jonathan Simm.

Key expert assistance was also provided by the following Posford Haskoning (Environment) staff: Stuart Cassie, Richard Cottle, Jonny Lewis, Elliot Newman, Lyall Seale, Robert Staniland and Peter Thornton. Design and illustrative input was provided by Maggie Morley.

The guide has benefited from invaluable assistance from experienced personnel within the construction industry. Accordingly, the authors wish to thank Kevin Howat and David Belsham (Edmund Nuttall Ltd), and Andy Baldwin and Peter Cross (Dean and Dyball Ltd).

Funders

The research leading to the publication of this site guide was funded by the:

- Department of Trade and Industry (DTI)

- Environment Agency

- English Nature

- Crown Estate

- Van Oord ACZ Ltd

- Royal Society for the Protection of Birds (RSPB)

- Department of the Marine and Natural Resources, Ireland.

Acknowledgements

Project Steering Group

CIRIA wishes to express its thanks to the members of the project steering group for their contributions to the work:

Roger Maddrell (Chairman)	Halcrow Group Ltd
Andy Baldwin	Dean & Dyball Construction Ltd
Tom Burke	Department of the Marine and Natural Resources
Victoria Cracknell	Environment Agency
Jason Golder	Crown Estate
John Goodwin	Van Oord ACZ Ltd
Duncan Huggett	RSPB
Christopher Pater	English Nature
Iain Roberts	Representative for the DTI (WS Atkins)

Thanks also go to the corresponding members of the project steering group:

David Belsham	Edmund Nuttall Ltd
Kate Cole	East Sussex County Council
Tony Cosgrove	English Nature
Robert Edgar	English Nature
Daniel Leggett	Babtie Group Ltd
Bob Lord	English Nature
Robin Hamilton	English Nature
Sarah-Jane Farr	Association of Local Government Archaeological Officers (ALGAO) Maritime Committee
Graham Lymbery	Sefton Metropolitan Borough Council
Alastair McNeill	Scottish Environment Protection Agency (SEPA)
Cath Ward	Blackpool Borough Council
Steve Waring	National Monuments Record Centre

CIRIA's Research Managers for this project were Daniel Leggett and Elizabeth Holliday.

Independent review was provided by David Murphy (Edmund Nuttall Ltd), John Davies (Sir Robert McAlpine Ltd) and Vicki Law (Sir Robert McAlpine Ltd).

The line drawing of a basking shark in Section 3.6.5 was provided by Ian Reach.

The target audience

Environmental issues will arise in any construction project, irrespective of the location, size or nature of the development. This is particularly true when considering the implications of working on the coast or at sea given the often sensitive nature of the habitats and the importance of this region for human activities and interests.

The task of preventing impacts or minimising the risk of potential implications is becoming increasingly the responsibility of front-line staff. This greater accountability at the site level demands higher standards of environmental awareness and education through trained and experienced personnel who can effectively manage environmental issues with the speed and urgency that they often require.

This guide provides practical and accessible information on appreciating, avoiding and mitigating the effects of poor environmental practice on coastal and marine construction projects. It is primarily aimed at:

- site managers, foremen and site supervisors
- site engineers
- contract supervisors/resident engineers
- project managers.

The guide is intended to be applicable to all levels of construction experience from the young site engineer to the experienced manager.

Adoption of the good practice presented in this guide by a broader group of construction professionals can also have a profound effect on construction activities and can affect the ability of site personnel to meet their obligations to the environment. Such professionals include:

- construction planners within contractors' main offices
- contractors
- project managers/directors
- designers
- clients
- local authority engineers
- construction managers
- planning supervisors and principal contractors
- environmental regulators.

Coverage of this guide

The guide addresses environmental issues once a project has reached the construction stage. For each of a series of key topics it describes potential impacts and indicates how they can be avoided or overcome.

The central focus of the guide is the coastal and marine environment. This area is taken to be the region where construction activities and development are most keenly affected by the sea. Equally, it is taken to be any area where construction activities can affect the sea directly or indirectly (eg spills, accidents etc).

The principal objectives of the guide are to:

- educate and inform front-line supervisors, engineers and managers working on coastal and marine construction projects about the environmental impacts associated with a range of common construction operations and activities

- provide guidance on avoiding or mitigating these environmental impacts

- summarise the generic requirements for project approval, so that front-line supervisors, engineers and managers are aware of environmental obligations put in place during the project approval process, people/bodies who have been consulted and documents they should expect to receive (eg Environmental Statements)

- improve the environmental performance of the construction industry working on coastal and marine projects

- provide guidance in an easily understandable and user-friendly format.

The reader should be clear about the limitations of the scope of the guide, in particular:

- It identifies risks but is not a health and safety manual (ie it is not a site safety guide).

- Use of the Guide should not replace consultation with regulatory and environmental authorities, and other key interested parties.

- The guide only summarises legislation. For more detail references have been provided but, in all cases, contact your company's environmental representative.

- In all instances when dealing with the issues covered, do not take action beyond your level of expertise. If in doubt, seek specialist advice.

- The guide does not address the entire scope of issues that are covered as part of the planning and design phases of the project. It is NOT a definitive guide to planning construction sites.

CIRIA Publication C584

How to use this guide

It is the intention of this document to provide guidance in a user-friendly and easily understandable format, acting as a reference book and training manual. The guide is structured into four main chapters, with **Chapter One** introducing the benefits of good environmental practice and why it should always be adopted.

Chapter Two identifies and details good (and bad) site management, providing evidence of how environmental disruption and damage can be quickly avoided through simple site management practices. This chapter also examines the risks of operating on the coast and at sea, illustrating the differences between working in this region and on land. The dynamic and uncertain nature of the seas provide a unique and constantly changing environment as well as forcing pressures and threats on man, machines and structures not faced elsewhere.

Chapter Three describes those environmental features (eg wildlife, water quality and noise) that require particular consideration when operating within the coastal and marine environment. Descriptions are given of the likely effects and risks to them arising from construction processes, the methods and measures by which these effects can be avoided and the emergency responses that may be required should an incident occur.

Finally, **Chapter Four** examines the 17 most common construction processes utilised in the coastal and marine environment and identifies how they are likely to impact upon the environment. Where relevant, the full nature of the impacts are described and a cross reference to the appropriate feature and section in other chapters is provided.

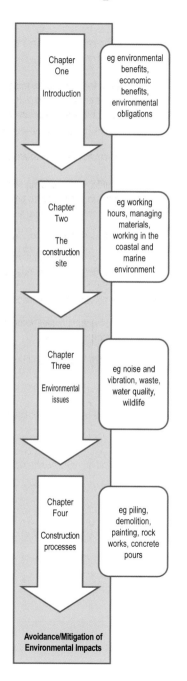

Chapter One

Introduction

eg environmental benefits, economic benefits, environmental obligations

Chapter Two

The construction site

eg working hours, managing materials, working in the coastal and marine environment

Chapter Three

Environmental issues

eg noise and vibration, waste, water quality, wildlife

Chapter Four

Construction processes

eg piling, demolition, painting, rock works, concrete pours

Avoidance/Mitigation of Environmental Impacts

How to use this guide

Please note that this guide is closely related to its "sister" document, the *Environmental good practice on site* handbook (CIRIA C502). To ensure that both books can be used simultaneously (where appropriate), the approach and format of this guide has remained consistent with that of the C502 handbook.

Throughout this guide, the following symbols have been used to help identify the types of information being provided and to simplify its use:

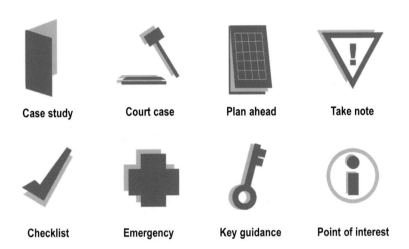

| Case study | Court case | Plan ahead | Take note |

| Checklist | Emergency | Key guidance | Point of interest |

Environmental authorities

This guide is aimed at construction operations in the coastal and marine environment as a whole and is applicable to all activities and processes in this region, irrespective of national and regional boundaries. To avoid confusion and to ensure that the guide is definitive in the information it provides, common references are used with respect to the representative authorities for environmental control and conservation.

The following table provides a list of the generic labels used in this guide and identifies those authorities referred to with regard to England, Wales, Scotland and Northern Ireland:

Reference used in text	England	Wales	Scotland	Northern Ireland
Environment Agency or Agencies	Environment Agency	Environment Agency	Scottish Environment Protection Agency (SEPA)	Environment and Heritage Service Northern Ireland (EHSNI)
Conservation Agency (see 3.6.2)	English Nature	Countryside Council for Wales (CCW)	Scottish Natural Heritage (SNH)	EHSNI
Environment Department	Department for Environment Food and Rural Affairs (DEFRA)	Welsh Assembly Government	The Scottish Executive Rural Affairs Department	Department of Agriculture and Rural Development Northern Ireland (DARNI)
Department for Local Government	The Office of the Deputy Prime Minister	Welsh Assembly Government	The Scottish Executive	Department of the Environment (DOE)

Environmental authorities

The good practice methods and techniques presented within this guide are generally appropriate for use in construction sites across the United Kingdom. However, as stated above, please note that there are legislative and regulatory variations between nations. Before anyone intends to implement the practices and procedures set out in this publication, they should ensure that the work recognises and complies with these variations. The relevant environment agency, conservation agency, Department for Local Government or your local authority will be able to advise on these matters.

At the time of writing, the main telephone numbers for the environment agencies are:

- Environment Agency, General Enquiry Line   0845 933 3111
- SEPA, Head Office, Stirling   01786 457 700
- Environment and Heritage Service, Belfast   028 9025 4754

The 24-Hour emergency hotline number for reporting all environmental incidents relating to air, land and water in England, Wales, Scotland and Northern Ireland is:

EMERGENCY HOTLINE

0800 80 70 60

If you require advice or assistance with regard to injured, distressed or dead animals found on or near to your site, please contact the Royal Society for the Prevention of Cruelty to Animals (RSPCA) or the Scottish Society for the Prevention of Cruelty to Animals (SSPCA).

RSPCA 0870 555 5999

SSPCA 0870 737 7722

Relationship to other CIRIA guidance

This guide should be read in conjunction with the CIRIA *Environmental good practice on site* handbook (C502) published in 1999. The handbook addresses issues in freshwater and terrestrial environments.

CIRIA has produced other key publications that establish the environmental issues to be taken into account during construction. These include:

- *A client's guide to greener construction,* SP120.

- *Control of water pollution from construction sites – guidance for consultants and contractors* (C532), Training materials (SP156).

- *Environmental handbook for building and civil engineering projects: Part 1, Design and specification* (C512), *Part 2, Construction phase* (C528), *Part 3, Demolition and Site Clearance* (C529).

- *Environmental management in construction,* C533.

CIRIA has also published a number of documents that relate to the issues, principles and legislation that should be adopted to improve environmental performance in the construction industry. Other CIRIA publications of particular relevance include:

- *Waste minimisation and recycling in construction: a review,* SP122. A detailed report of waste minimisation and recycling in construction.

- *Waste minimisation in construction – site guide,* SP133. This outlines current good practice in site waste management and contains information on reducing wastage of raw materials, and reusing and recycling waste materials.

- *The observational method in ground engineering: principles and applications,* R185. This is specifically relevant to minimising waste in ground engineering and to optimising design to foresee problems on site.

- *Managing materials and components on site,* SP146. A site guide that provides practical guidance for site managers, site engineers and supervisors on how to manage materials and components effectively.

- *Environmental issues in construction – a desk study,* PR73. A review of published research and the response of the industry to environmental issues.

Further details on the above and other CIRIA publications can be obtained from:

6 Storey's Gate, Westminster, London, SW1P 3AU; Telephone 020 7222 8891; Fax 020 7222 1708; email: enquiries@ciria.org.uk or visit the CIRIA website at www.ciria.org.uk

Contents

Contents

Glossary

Archaeology
Historic and prehistoric remains, often discovered by excavation and found on construction sites.

Benthos
Those animals and plants on or near to the seabed.

Biodiversity
The richness and variety of wildlife and habitats on earth.

Built environment
Developed areas, including residential, commercial and industrial property.

CADW
The name CADW comes from the Welsh word that means "to keep" or "to preserve". CADW is the organisation responsible for protecting, conserving and presenting ancient monuments and historic buildings in Wales.

Cliffs and slopes
Cliffs and slopes comprise sloping to vertical faces on the coastline where a break in slope is formed by slippage and/or coastal erosion.

Conservation
Active management of the earth's natural resources and environment to ensure quality is maintained and that they are wisely used, whilst acknowledging the dynamic character of biological and physical systems.

Contamination
The presence of a sufficient quantity of a substance in land, water or air making it capable of causing significant harm.

Controlled waters
Virtually all natural waters in the UK, including coastal and estuarine waters up to 3 km offshore, rivers, streams, ditches, ponds and ground waters. Responsibility for policing controlled waters lies with the relevant environment agencies.

Dewatering
The removal of ground water or surface water to lower the water table.

Discharge consent
Permission to discharge effluent, subject to conditions laid down in the consent, as issued by the relevant environment agency.

Dunes
Area of sand blown by wind into small hills and ridges with particular plant communities.

Dust
Airborne solid matter up to about 2 mm in size.

Ecology
Study of the relationships between organisms and the relationship between them and their physical environment.

Environmental Action Plan
A report which ensures commitment to the adoption of mitigation and management measures, as recommended within the ES.

Environmental Impact Assessment
A procedure employed to assess the likely significant impacts of a proposed development upon the environment.

Glossary

Environmental Statement	The report or final set of documents which contain the findings and recommendations of the EIA procedure.
Fauna	The animal life of a region or a particular environment.
Flora	The plants of a region or a particular environment (eg saltmarsh flora).
Geomorphology	The study of the physical features of the Earth's surface and their formation (ie processes of erosion and deposition).
Groundwater	The water in the ground.
Habitat	The particular environment in which an organism or a group of organisms live.
Intertidal	The zone between high and low tide marks that varies in extent along the coast.
Invertebrates	Animals that lack a back-bone, including insects, worms, crustaceans and molluscs.
Maintenance (plant and vehicles)	The general task of ensuring that construction plant and vehicles are kept "roadworthy" and capable of undertaking their allotted tasks.
Maintenance (works)	The construction and re-construction activities required in order to keep a built structure or commenced scheme operational.
Mudflat	An area of fine silt (mud) usually exposed at low tide but covered at high tide. Typically occurs in sheltered estuaries and can occur behind shingle bars or sand spits.
Natural environment	The composition of wildlife and habitats.
Noise	Sounds that are undesired or cause nuisance to local residents and businesses. Noise is measured in decibels (dB)
Offshore	That area of sea beyond the land which has depths in excess of 20 m.
Organism	Any single living plant or animal.
Pollution	Introducing substances or energy (eg noise) to land, water or air that are likely to cause significant harm to humans, wildlife and/or buildings. Pollutants include silty water, heavy metals, sewage, oils, chemicals, litter, clays and mud.
Recycling	Collecting and separating materials from waste and processing them to produce marketable products.
Reuse	Putting objects back into use, without processing, so that they do not remain in the waste stream.

Glossary

Risk	The chance of an adverse event actually occurring.
Saltmarsh	A coastal or estuarine area vegetated by salt tolerant plants.
Sediments	The layers of particles that cover the bottom of the seabed and other water-bodies, such as rivers and streams.
Shingle	Shingle is defined as sediment with particle sizes in the range 2–200 mm. Shingle structures take the form either of spits, barrier islands or of cuspate forelands.
Silt	Waterborne particles with a very small grain size.
Species	A group of organisms that interbreed.
Subtidal	The region of the sea and the seabed that occurs beneath the tidal zone.
Tide	The periodic rise and fall in the level of water in the oceans and sea, resulting from the gravitational attraction of the sun and the moon.
Turbidity	The interference of the passage of sunlight through the water column caused by the presence of fine suspended matter (eg silt, sand).
Tremie	A method of concrete placement that utilises a long funnel, which is hung from a crane, one end of which is placed underwater where the concrete will be placed.
UK waters	These include territorial waters, whose limits extend to 12 nautical miles offshore, and waters to 200 nautical miles offshore within which the UK exercises certain rights and jurisdictions.
Vegetated shingle	Shingle supporting a wildlife community of flora and fauna.
Waste	Any substance or object that the holder discards, intends to discard or is required to discard.
Wildlife	Wild animals and birds.

Abbreviations

ALGAO	Association of Local Government Archaeological Officers
AONB	Area of Outstanding Natural Beauty
ASSI	Area of Special Scientific Interest
BMAPA	British Marine Aggregate Producers Association
BPM	Best Practicable Means
BRE	Buildings Research Establishment
BS	British Standard
BSI	British Standards Institute
CADW	Welsh Historic Monuments
CCTV	Closed Circuit Television
CCW	Countryside Council for Wales
CDM	Construction (Design and Management) Regulations (1994)
CERC	Coastal Engineering Research Centre
CIRIA	The Construction Industry Research and Information Association
COPA	Control of Pollution Act (1974)
CROW	Countryside and Rights of Way Act (2000)
CUR	Centre for Civil Engineering Research and Codes
DARNI	Department for Agriculture and Rural Development
dB	Decibel
DEFRA	Department for Environment, Food and Rural Affairs
DETR	Department of Environment, Transport and the Regions
DOE	Department of the Environment (Northern Ireland)
DTi	Department of Trade and Industry
EAP	Environmental Action Plan
EC	European Community
EIA	Environmental Impact Assessment
EMAS	Eco-Management Audit System
EMS	Environmental Management System
EPA	Environmental Protection Act (1990)
ES	Environmental Statement

Abbreviations

FEPA	Food and Environmental Protection Act (1985)
GCRS	Geological Conservation Review Site
H&S	Health and Safety
HSE	Health and Safety Executive
ISO	International Organisation for Standardisation
JNCC	Joint Nature Conservation Committee
LNR	Local Nature Reserve
MNR	Marine Nature Reserve
NNR	National Nature Reserve
ODPM	Office of the Deputy Prime Minister
PPE	Personal Protective Equipment
RCA	Recipient Competent Authority (Licence)
RCHME	Royal Commission on the Historical Monuments of England
RSPB	The Royal Society for the Protection of Birds
RSPCA	The Royal Society for the Prevention of Cruelty to Animals
SAC	Special Area of Conservation
SAM	Scheduled Ancient Monument
SEPA	Scottish Environment Protection Agency
SMC	Scheduled Monument Consent
SNH	Scottish Natural Heritage
SPA	Special Protection Area
SSPCA	Scottish Society for the Prevention of Cruelty to Animals
SSSI	Site of Special Scientific Interest
TBT	Tributyltin
WWF	World Wildlife Fund for Nature

1 Introduction

1.1 Introduction

1.1 Background

A great deal of published guidance on the effects of construction activities on the environment already exists, although this is predominantly focused on land-based sites.

As a result, and following discussions with industry and other stakeholders, CIRIA considered that there was an absence of information relating to coastal and marine construction activities, especially in a format that is suitable for use on site and easy to access in an emergency situation. As such, the objective of this guide is to fill this void and to ensure that coastal and marine site personnel have the correct information to hand for dealing with key environmental and management issues.

1.2 The benefits

The adverse effects of construction on the coastal and marine environment are well publicised and understood by regulators, the industry and the general public. Badly planned and unmanaged sites can have a multitude of adverse effects on the natural, human and built environment.

Within the industrial sector of England and Wales, the greatest identified contributor to pollution incidents in 2000 was the construction industry, with 16% (854) of total incidents (Environment Agency 2001).

The impact of poor working practices on the coastal and marine environment can be extensive, particularly given the often sensitive nature of the habitats and the potential for far reaching effects (eg drift of spills on currents). The working environment is also vastly different from that found on land, with winds, waves, currents, tides and storm events making this region difficult to forecast and, ultimately, more risky and uncertain to operate within (ie further increasing the likelihood of accidents and environmental damage).

Given current awareness of environmental matters, it is now accepted good practice to seek environmental improvements within all aspects of the construction industry. This is for two reasons: they bring environmental and economic benefits.

CIRIA Publication C584

The benefits 1.2

Environmental benefits

Better environmental performance means:

- **Reduced damage to the coastal and marine environment** – Uncontrolled construction activities can have a significant effect on habitats sensitive to the influence of man, such as saltmarsh, offshore reefs and their associated flora and fauna.

- **Reduced demand for natural resources** – The construction industry is a major user of natural resources such as hardwood timber, quarried rock, sand and gravel. These materials are not renewable and the associated extraction processes result in environmental impacts themselves.

- **Reduced disruption to local residents and businesses** – Construction sites on the coast and at sea can be visually intrusive and, more immediately, affect locals and tourists through increased noise, vibration, dust and traffic levels. By complaining or taking action, local residents may delay the project and increase costs.

- **Meeting the requirements of recognised standards** – The increasing use of Environmental Management Systems (EMS) within companies, to achieve recognised standards such as ISO 14001, requires better appreciation of good practice and environmental responsibility on site.

Economic benefits

The economic benefits of environmental good practice are also important. Implementation does not need to be costly and sound environmental practice makes good economic sense. The economic benefits resulting can include, but are not limited to:

- **Less money wasted on fines** – Fines for pollution incidents and/or damage to protected sites are enforced. Added to the legal costs and management time lost to the procedure, the overall penalty can be major.

> One utility company concluded that pollution incidents could reduce shareholder value by around £3.5 million over 10 years. based on fines of £90 000 per annum (not including intangible costs).

- **Fewer resources directed at restoration** – Cleaning up after pollution incidents or repairing damage to habitats can be expensive, requiring significant resources from both management and external specialists (eg ecological skills).

> The proposed EU Directive on environmental liability intends to provide a framework for the restoration (including compensation measures) of significant damage to internationally protected habitats and species, and "controlled" waters.

- **Investment and funding procedures** – More than 60% of the largest UK pension funds and local authority funds indicated that they would invest only in socially responsible schemes. These bodies are increasingly aware of environmental, social and ethical considerations and, more importantly, the pressures that are imposed on today's natural and human environment.

- **Reducing risks** – Improving working practices and management on site will reduce risk. This is particularly important in the coastal and marine environment, where sea and weather conditions can dramatically affect construction operations.

- **Improved opportunities to tender** – It is common for prospective clients to choose contractors based, amongst other things, on their environmental track record and achieved standards. Not being accredited to ISO 14001 or having a "record" for offences will often preclude organisations from being invited to tender.

- **Market image** – Improved environmental performance will result in an improved image with clients, employees, sub-contractors and the market (ie the general public). Not only will this be of benefit in terms of relationships with regulatory authorities, but it will allow projects to run more smoothly on a day-to-day basis.

1.3   Environmental obligations

In addition to the environmental and economic benefits gained from implementing good practice on coastal and marine construction sites, there are a number of legislative and contractual controls that demand good practice be followed:

- **National legislation** – In place to protect overall environmental quality (ie water, air and land) and the natural (ie habitats and species) and human (ie public access and archaeology) environment from the effects of development and land use change

> Within the UK, the regulation of the environment is politically devolved, meaning that in some cases distinct differences in national legislation may be apparent. Similarly, the regulatory bodies responsible for its enforcement may also differ. Whilst it is not necessarily important that you intimately understand the variations in legislation, it is imperative that you recognise the implications of breaching regulations.

Environmental obligations

In England and Wales, the control of water pollution is the responsibility of the Environment Agency, under the Environmental Protection Act 1990 and the Water Resources Act 1991. Local authorities have more responsibility over noise, air and soil pollution, again under the Environment Protection Act, but also under the Control of Pollution Act (COPA) 1974 and the Clean Air Act 1993.

In Scotland and Northern Ireland, the same responsibilities lie with the Scottish Environment Protection Agency (SEPA) and the Environment and Heritage Service respectively, under separate legislation;

Natural heritage issues fall within the remit of the relevant conservation agency. Under legislation, sites may be designated and protected by virtue of their ecological, archaeological, geological or geomorphological interest;

Regulatory controls for issues such as planning permission, harbour works or dredging of the sea bed fall under the responsibility of other bodies, including local authorities, harbour authorities and the relevant environment department (ie Department for Environment, Food and Rural Affairs (DEFRA) for works below mean high water in England).

- **Specifications and contract conditions** – The characteristics of the proposed development or activity, and its likely impact on the immediate coastal and marine environment, will have been identified during the planning and design process. Subject to the findings of the planning process and any commitments made by the developer to the local community, conditions will usually have been assigned to the contract prior to the commencement of construction.

> Contract conditions can include, for example, stipulating that works do not occur during "anti-social" hours (ie 7 pm to 8 am), to minimise disruption to residents, wildlife and/or businesses. However, this particular condition is not always an option in the coastal and marine environment, given the working requirements imposed by the tides.

- **Local control** – There may be a number of requirements imposed on construction works by local authorities through the powers given to them in national legislation. This could come from responsibilities under COPA.

- **Estuarine partnerships and coastal fora** – Although without legal status, estuarine and coastal zone partnerships often include local authority, Environment Agency and conservation agency members. Contractors should aim to consult with these organisations on likely construction impacts and local issues, where appropriate.

1.4 Coastal and marine environment

- **Corporate control** – The growing adoption of corporate environmental policies, EMS and site-specific environmental plans requires good practice on construction sites.

> It is the responsibility of the developer to ensure that all consents are in place before construction begins. However, it is also the responsibility of the contractors to ensure that they have seen these consents (and obtained a copy) and are aware of any relevant conditions before going on site.

In the coastal and marine environment the following consents may be applicable:

- Coast Protection Act (1949) consent
- Food and Environment Protection Act (FEPA) (1985) licence
- Planning permission under the Town and Country Planning Regulations (1997)
- Planning permission under the Harbours Act (1964)
- A consent for temporary or permanent abstraction or discharge to controlled waters under the Water Resources Act (1991)
- Consent from the sewerage operator, where appropriate
- Agreement from the statutory conservation agency under the Wildlife and Countryside Act (1981), as amended by the Countryside and Rights of Way Act (CROW) (2000), and the Nature Conservation and Amenity Lands Order (1985)
- The Conservation (Natural Habitats &c) Regulations (1994)
- Transport and Works Act (1992)
- Electricity Act (1989).

Further detail on these permissions and consents, and the legislative differences between nations in the UK, can be provided by the planning department within your local authority or by your company's environmental representative. Guidance on environmental legislation can also be found on the "NETREG" area of the environment agencies web sites (eg http://www.environment-agency.gov.uk/netregs).

1.4 The coastal and marine environment

What geographical region are we talking about when we think of the *coastal and marine environment?*

The coast can be defined as that area where water, land and air meet, and where processes occur to form landscapes unlike those found anywhere else. It is not strictly a boundary, rather a zone or a region where the influences of the sea and man are most

Coastal and marine environment 1.4

evident. Examples of construction schemes on the coast include beach nourishment, port and harbour developments, and sea defences.

The marine environment is that area beyond the land and the coast which comprises open water (ie the sea). Much like the coast, this region is highly dynamic, offering a variety of operating conditions and risks. Examples of offshore construction schemes include oil and gas platforms, wind farm developments and the laying of cables, pipelines and long-sea outfalls.

For the purposes of this Guide, the coastal and marine environment is taken to be that region where construction activities and development are most affected by the sea. Equally, it is also taken to be that area where those same activities can influence or are likely to impact upon the sea (ie spills, accidents etc). As such, this equates to activities undertaken in, under or on the following areas (as examples):

● sand dunes	● saltmarsh	● spits
● beaches	● cliffs	● estuaries
● sand banks	● shore platforms	● mud flats
● seabed	● islands	● promenades/paths
● piers and jetties	● breakwaters	● dock walls
● revetments	● rigs and platforms	● marine vessels

The nature and characteristics of the coastal and marine environment mean that operating on the coast or at sea presents construction personnel with a changing and vastly different environment from that faced by their counterparts in-land (as described in C502). The very elements that help to make the coast what it is, produce the risks and problems that are encountered in the marine environment.

A more detailed description of these parameters is provided in Section 2.2.1 but, in summary, they are:

● waves

● tides

● currents

● winds

● any combination of the above.

1.5 Schemes and processes

The coastal and marine environment and some of its composite parts and features

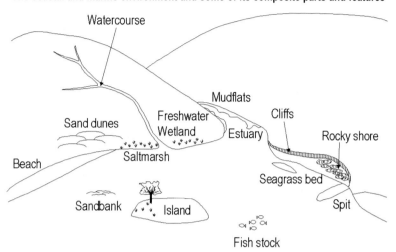

Fish stock

1.5 Schemes and processes

The coastal and marine environment provides great stimuli for development, activities and interest by its very nature. The influence of man in this environment is greatly felt, particularly in estuarine areas where shelter and deeper water are sometimes provided. The principal types of development that are undertaken in the coastal and marine environment are:

- docks, harbours and ports
- marinas and recreational centres
- flood defences and coastal protection
- estuarine barriers and barrages
- pipelines and cables
- outfalls and intakes
- dredging for marine materials and navigation
- renewable energy sources, including wind farms and tidal power
- oil and gas exploration and extraction
- infrastructure for land transport, such as bridges and tunnels
- other built developments (ie housing, commercial centres etc).

 CIRIA Publication C584

Schemes and processes

Coastal and marine schemes and their (typical) locations

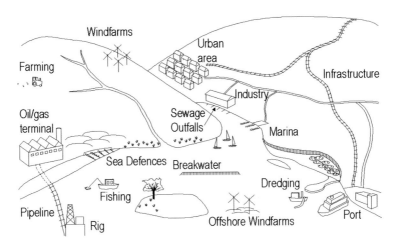

In total, 17 construction processes have been identified that are common to the construction and performance of these schemes. These processes are described in more detail in Chapter Four of this Guide but, in summary, are:

Construction processes in the coastal and marine environment

1. Demolition
2. Dredging
3. Excavation
4. Drilling and blasting underwater
5. Installation of pipelines and cables
6. Nourishment and reclamation
7. Geotextiles
8. Rock works/placement of concrete units
9. Timber works
10. Piling
11. Masonry
12. Painting
13. Grouting (and tremie concreting)
14. Concrete pours and aftercare
15. Asphalt works
16. Marine vessels and plant, inc maintenance
17. Land based plant, inc. maintenance

Please note that "construction" is not just about the initial building phase of a development, it also relates to maintenance works or phases of re-construction that occur after operations have commenced. As such, the content and recommendations of this guide are directed at all phases of construction, regardless of when they are undertaken.

2 The construction site

This chapter provides details of good practice in setting up and managing construction sites in the coastal and marine environment. Particular attention is given to the uncertainty and risks of working in this environment, the problems that might be encountered and how they can be overcome.

2.1 The management framework

If you are to deal effectively with environmental issues on your construction site, what do you need to have in place from the beginning, even before going onto site?

2.1.1 Setting the scene

Effective environmental management on site requires a team effort. This includes input from the main contractor and sub-contractors on site, your own organisation (off-site) and from third-party organisations involved in the project (eg the designer, client and suppliers). This process can be significantly improved by working in partnership with the relevant statutory conservation and environment agencies.

To manage this teamwork effectively, the **site manager** (who is responsible for any sub-contractors on site) should follow the steps outlined below:

STEP 1   *Establish the environmental obligations of the project*

STEP 2   *Identify the environmental hazards and sensitivities particular to the site*

Steps 1 and 2 can be achieved through reviewing relevant design, planning and contract documentation (particularly any Environmental Statements (ES) or Environmental Action Plans (EAP) – see Section 2.1.7), and through discussions with your company's environmental representative, the local authority and, where appropriate, the relevant environment agency.

- Become familiar with all aspects of your site, especially those features or parameters of noted sensitivity, and how they might be affected by construction.

- Pre-construction phases such as design and planning may have identified specific environmentally sensitive areas, such as unique species, threatened habitats, adjacent settlements and/or other human interests (ie cultural heritage). These sensitivities may require special construction procedures or the design of temporary works, which in turn will require specially trained staff and working knowledge.

- Call upon your own and your team's experience of similar sites and environments. Use specialists, particularly where sensitivities require them.

> The earlier a contractor can be brought into the scheme, the better. They can significantly aid in pre-construction planning and the design phases, adding their knowledge and site experience to the development of the project.

STEP 3   *Establish an environmental management structure and plan*

- It is important to define the environmental responsibilities of all personnel within the site management structure, including those involved in monitoring initiatives (see Section 2.1.3 for further detail). Once determined, the names, roles and responsibilities of staff should be recorded, along with the environmental procedures in place for dealing with potential issues. The level of detail in this plan will depend on the complexity and size of the development and should define lines of communication between all staff and third parties (ie regulators), as well as providing contact and emergency details.

- The site environmental plan must be accessible and regularly revised. All site staff, third parties and visitors to the works must be aware of its existence and importance to the safeguarding of the local environment.

STEP 4   *Train your personnel*

- Environmental responsibilities need to be in place at all levels of an organisation since it only takes one act of ignorance or non-compliance to cause damage.

- Appropriate training of personnel and a clear definition of responsibilities will help to minimise the potential for accidents to occur. Also, explain why safeguarding the environment is important, it should not be seen as a chore or burden to normal day-to-day activities (see Section 2.1.5).

STEP 5   *Monitor actions and effects*

- Environmental monitoring of the coastal and marine environment is more likely to be required where significant potential impacts have been identified during project planning. This monitoring may be carried out by regulators, but can also be undertaken by developers, where appropriate.

- Site managers should undertake their own monitoring of the construction area to ensure good practice through the inspection of working practices, site conditions and/or visible damage to features etc. Such monitoring will help to identify where training and instruction has helped to safeguard the environment and, equally, where it has not (or could be improved or is not included).

2.1.2 The regulatory agencies

Whatever the size of the project, it will be necessary to communicate with the relevant regulatory authorities, whether at a national, regional or local level. These bodies have a diverse range of specific responsibilities and powers to enforce legislation. Their responsibilities are as follows:

Regulators	Responsibility
Local authority	Noise, air quality, traffic, considerate contractors schemes, ground contamination, landscape and aesthetics, designation of Local Nature Reserves.
Environmental agencies	Waste, effluent discharges, Part B authorisations for air quality (SEPA), abstraction licences (England and Wales only), some nature conservation functions.
Statutory conservation agency (ie English Nature, CCW, SEPA and Environment and Heritage Service)	Designated ecological sites, geological and geomorphological sites, protected species and habitats.
County archaeologist Heritage bodies	Designated archaeological and heritage sites, landscape and aesthetics.
Health and Safety Executive Maritime and Coastguard Agency	Health and safety. Response to spills.

It is always advisable to contact the regulatory agencies as early as possible to discuss the project with them. Regulatory authorities welcome an early approach and will be able to advise on environmental issues of local importance that should be included in the identification of the project's environmental sensitivities (Step 2 of establishing the environmental framework for the site). This is particularly relevant for projects where an Environmental Impact Assessment (EIA) has not been undertaken.

It is important to develop a constant and constructive dialogue with the officers of the regulatory authorities monitoring a project. Explain what is happening on the project and why. This may simplify approval procedures and is likely to be helpful if things do go wrong, as you will know whom to speak to.

Checklist – dealing with regulatory agencies

- Plan ahead. Try to avoid problems and give regulators advanced warning of potential problems.

- Give regulators the time they need to process your enquiry.

- Always display prominently the relevant emergency number for the regulatory authorities.

- Make sure that all site personnel and visitors to the site know the correct procedures for reporting incidents – they should let the site manager know before contacting the relevant regulatory authorities.

- Always notify the relevant environment agency of any contaminating spill.

2.1.3 Management responsibilities

Ensuring environmental good practice is no different from any other task on site. In order that it can happen, and for the works to comply with legislation, responsibilities need to be defined and understood by everyone. A sound approach is to ensure that environmental good practice starts at the top of the company in a similar way to good health and safety practice. Certain individuals will have clearly defined roles but everyone on site is responsible for ensuring that their actions constitute good practice. A typical working arrangement for environmental management on site is outlined below.

Full-time site-based **environmental posts** are not usually necessary, typically responsibilities for environmental issues can be included within the responsibilities of existing staff. However, increasingly, medium to large sized contractors are creating a full-time head office post for an environmental manager and on large projects environment site officers (often part time), are nominated.

On most projects, regardless of their size, the **site manager** (or site agent) has principal responsibility for environmental management on that project. They may decide to define, monitor and control environmental practice themselves, or they may select a **delegated representative** to act on their behalf. Responsibility for environmental management will include auditing environmental practice, liaising with regulatory authorities, and informing and monitoring sub-contractors. Many companies have taken the opportunity of using their safety inspectors as environmental inspectors as well. The benefits are that a pool of expertise is developed and good practice can be easily shared around sites.

Site engineers and/or **site foremen** are usually in the best position to put the environmental plan into practice. They need to understand the relevant environmental obligations and the practical measures needed to comply with them. On large sites the plan can be subdivided, with a different engineer responsible for each section.

For example, one person may be designated as the waste site manager, another may be in charge of noise control and so on.

The engineers should then provide feedback to the site manager, allowing for a consistent and thorough on-site approach.

Site foremen and **supervisors** should ensure that environmental controls are implemented at the workface. They can best undertake this responsibility through working closely with all site workers. Together, the foremen should review the training that site personnel need and be instrumental in arranging for this to be provided.

On all sites, irrespective of their size, all site personnel must be charged with following good practice and encouraged to provide feedback and suggestions for improvements.

Prominent and clear signage is a good way of raising staff awareness

 Successful environmental management relies on communication. It is crucial that everyone is aware of the key issues, has the relevant information to deal with them, understands their responsibilities and provides feedback to those in charge.

All site personnel must know whom they can contact for advice on managing environmental issues and whom they can ask for training. Feedback down the chain is important in maintaining motivation and raising awareness.

Responsibility for environmental good practice does not rest at the site level. In larger companies, a main board member may be responsible for directing and reviewing corporate environmental protocols and responsibilities. In smaller companies, this responsibility may be held by the managing director. It is good practice to appoint someone to be responsible for providing corporate advice on environmental legislation, good practice and the company's environmental policy.

Whatever the company structure, it is vital that **intermediate management** translates decisions into action at site level.

The management responsibilities presented here for main contractors should also apply to all sub-contractors, whatever their size. However, please note that overall responsibility still rests with the main contractor.

2.1.4 Managing your sub-contractors

The environmental awareness of sub-contractors varies considerably. Some may be particularly conscientious, whilst others may assume that all responsibility rests with the main contractor on site. The task of the site manager is to ensure that sub-contractors understand their obligations and meet them. As with any controls, environmental responsibility can be implemented with incentives or penalties. The following checklist presents suggestions for selecting, motivating and managing sub-contractors.

You may be held responsible for your sub-contractors' offences if you do not exercise reasonable control over them.

Checklist – Managing your sub-contractor

- Ensure that sub-contractors are aware of the environmental management requirements of the site, before commencing work.

- If the sub-contractor works frequently with the main contractor, then it is common for the main contractor to invite (or require) them to attend environmental training sessions.

- Ensure that the sub-contractors are aware of the environmental obligations of the project.

- When selecting sub-contractors, ask them to present proof of their past record in achieving good environmental practice. Stipulate that records of environmental prosecutions will be taken into account.

- Include environmental controls from the project specification in the sub-contract, and encourage the use of method statements, to ensure good environmental practice.

2.1.5 Raising awareness

It is important to raise awareness of environmental issues so that people on site understand what environmental good practice is, are aware of its benefits and know where to obtain further information. Training should be provided company-wide to spread good practice generally and at a site level to address issues relevant to a particular construction project.

2.1 The management framewor

For a successful training programme it is vital to:

- initiate local level training as early as possible (ie before walking on site)
- select the right trainer, preferably from your own company
- select the audience
- tailor the level of detail provided to the audience
- ensure that the material presented is relevant and focused
- follow up and enforce training as necessary (ie based on site manager monitoring and the turnover of staff).

> Sound environmental management comes from knowing what to do and developing the right attitudes.

It is very useful to give site personnel environmental training alongside their induction to health and safety on site. The sooner you highlight identified risks on site, and the correct working practices to be followed, the better your chances are of avoiding an emergency or environmental problem.

For training purposes, checklist and guidance cards could be provided to site staff to help them in their day-to-day work. These cards can be kept in the central office or in work huts, vehicles and on notice boards (if laminated) for easy use.

In order to be effective, adequate time should be set aside to inform staff about the environmental issues that

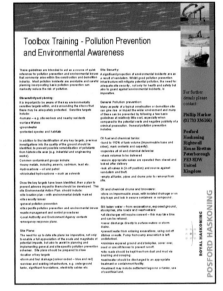

are relevant to their site and to their work. CIRIA, in conjunction with the Environment Agency, has produced a video, leaflet and poster set that may be useful for on-site training – *Building a cleaner future*, CIRIA SP141.

Key training topics for site managers and engineers

- the reasons for adopting good practice
- good practice in dealing with potential pollutants (eg oil refuelling, handling of paints and solvents)
- how to manage wastes
- how to manage materials and components on site to reduce wastage
- emergency procedures and contact details
- choice of working methods, and sources of advice
- relevant legislation
- choice of plant
- importance of good housekeeping
- personal responsibility/liability.

2.1.6 Liasing with clients and designers

Although all environmental obligations should be included within the contract, drawings or specification, it is worth checking whether any information has been inadvertently omitted. For example, legislative acts are often quoted without the accompanying obligations being identified. This guide will help you to understand what information you will be looking for, but remember, if in doubt, also to ask your company's environmental representative.

An on-site meeting between the designer and contractor and, if appropriate consultants, at the start of the contract may be useful to help the contractor understand where environmental issues may have affected the design.

> If you feel that the design of temporary or permanent works does not conform with environmental good practice, refer it back to the designer or client.

Where the contract documents impose restrictive environmental conditions, it is often worth discussing with the designers or "specifiers" the reasons for the conditions. It may be possible to explore alternative approaches that have the same (or lower) environmental impacts. For example, can bored piles be used instead of driven piles to reduce noise and vibration?

Where a project has undergone a full or partial EIA there will be a considerable amount of information on the environmental issues surrounding the site.

In these circumstances, it is worth requesting that the client or designer gives a presentation to key staff on the environmental background to the project or provide an EAP that summarises the assessment.

2.1.7 Environmental management systems (EMS)

It is important to have a mechanism to distribute instructions and information throughout a company, to check whether these are being followed, and that their objectives are being achieved.

An EMS is the mechanism by which a company sets, monitors and achieves environmental targets. This includes the definition of management responsibilities and reporting procedures. The site environmental plan (introduced in Section 2.1.1) can arrange the management and reporting procedures on site to mirror those of an EMS. However, if an EMS is in place, the primary purpose of the site plan is to focus on the environmental issues specific to the site.

There are two main environmental standards for EMS within the UK – ISO 14001 and EMAS (European Community Eco-Management and Audit Scheme). In many ways these systems are very similar to the quality management system (ISO 9000), implemented by most companies.

Environmental management plans

Environmental Management Plans are an effective way of employing the principles of EMS at the site level. These may be a requirement of the organisation's environmental policy or the contract may well impose specific or general environmental requirements on the contractor (and/or sub-contractors). In either case, project and site managers will need to acquaint themselves, through the environmental management plan, with the environmental requirements of the contract or their company, and will need to ensure awareness of these issues among their staff and workforce.

The benefits of environmental management plans
• introduces a planning phase before undertaking the project
• raises awareness and focuses training
• records environmental performance during the construction phase, allowing for modification and improvement of working practice
• provides for site specific purchasing policies
• provides for transport policies, including selection and maintenance of site plant/vehicles
• allows careful control of working hours
• helps to minimise energy use

The benefits of environmental management plans (cont.)

- helps to minimise water use
- improves waste management, storage, reuse and recycling
- creates strategies for dealing with sensitive features and areas such as archaeology, ecology, and nature conservation sites, including SSSIs
- helps sub-contractor management.

Environmental Action Plans (EAP)

EAPs are designed to facilitate the transfer of environmental recommendations from an EIA (reported in an ES) into the detailed design, construction and maintenance phases of a project. In the construction phase, this will usually consist of a list of site specific actions to be carried out prior to, during and following construction. These are likely to be part of the contract for the project. It is essential that all of those actions that fall on the contractor are addressed prior to work commencing and that clear responsibility is assigned. EAPs will often be provided to the contractor by the client, or their consultants, and will assign actions to all parties (ie contractor, client, regulator etc). Work should not progress until you are satisfied that all necessary actions have been progressed.

2.2 Working in the coastal and marine environment

Operating on the coast and at sea places construction activities and personnel into a vastly different working arena from that faced on land. There are many similarities, but it is the dynamic and changing forces of the sea that set the two apart. Waves, tides, currents and winds provide a plethora of risks and issues that need to be overcome if an operation is to proceed satisfactorily (ie in terms of both site staff and the environment).

This section outlines the parameters that managers and site staff should consider both at the start of a project and in every-day operations when working on the coast or at sea. Guidance is provided along with a description of some of the ways in which these parameters can be forecast, in order to reduce risks, increase site safety and reduce environmental impacts.

The differences in marine operating conditions, compared to those inland, are due mainly to wind, waves, tides and currents. For all of these, a proper operating plan needs to be in place. Whilst this is a requirement of the CDM Health and Safety Plan, it will also ensure better protection of the coastal and marine environment (ie accidents lead to spills).

Working in the coastal and marine environment

2.2.1 Plan for weather and sea conditions

It is important to plan for weather and sea conditions given:

- the variability and severity of the conditions that could potentially arise
- the risks of loss and damage
- the associated delay, costs and impacts if contingencies are not in place.

Coastal and marine weather and sea conditions – the driving forces

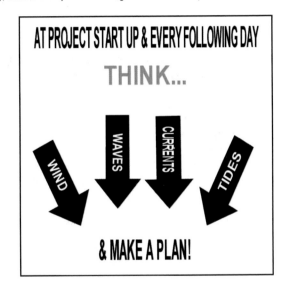

Winds can be particularly strong at the coastline. Winds are of the order of 10% faster over water than over land and the lack of shelter when the winds are from offshore will exacerbate this effect. Wind chill and driving rains can be significant factors for site personnel and can restrict the operation of all land-based plant. High rainfall can also affect working conditions, adding to flooding of the site and damaging concrete and other materials.

Wind can also have an important effect on floating craft. The effect of strong and rapidly varying wind-speeds and local pressures can cause significant motion, affecting operations. The local wind climate will also drive the wave climate, with the exception of swell conditions that generally originate from more distant storms.

Working in the coastal and marine environment

Tides will define what works can be carried out in the dry and the access time available to them. They can:

- prevent sea borne deliveries from reaching the site
- greatly restrict land access to site
- flood the works where excavations or cofferdams are used
- affect the wave and current climate that can penetrate into a construction site from the open sea.

Also, in simple terms, at the shore: **Higher tides = larger waves**

This means that at high tide, during the elevation of water levels due to storm surge and wind/wave set-up, the site is at its most vulnerable.

 It is essential to obtain forecasts early and plan your works accordingly. Remember that you may have to work with the tide. What are the implications for your site?

Tide levels can vary greatly from one location to another, with enormous ranges noted between spring (highest) and neap (lowest) tides. For example, in the estuary of the River Severn, the tidal range can be as much as 15.4 m, whilst on the east coast of the UK ranges can be as small as 1–2 m.

Waves can:

- affect deliveries reaching the site (eg preventing barges from leaving port, causing them to "run for shelter", delaying them in transit and preventing them from unloading etc)
- damage plant (due to beaching, overturning, striking the works etc)
- damage temporary and incomplete works where permanent protection is not yet in place
- draw-down beach levels which can affect the works, deliveries and expose contaminated materials
- result in poor placement of material, which may affect the environment.

Currents can:

- affect the ability of a vessel to hold position offshore
- affect the ability of a vessel to safely approach the site, especially in restricted water depth
- affect the ability to place materials within tolerance
- erode partially completed works
- apply loading on temporary works
- affect the incident wave conditions
- increase turbidity of the water, resulting in damage to flora and fauna.

2.2.2 Increased knowledge and guidance

The Wind Climate

Wind velocities over water can be obtained from ship observations or from the archives of weather models. In both of these cases, individual records may be unreliable but the large volume of data makes them a good source of site-specific ocean wind climate data. Around most of the UK coast, sequential wind records (digital) are available in England and Wales from the Meteorological Office).

Wind climate data can be expressed as a scatter diagram of wind-speed against direction or as a wind rose, see below. Typically wind velocities will be divided into Beaufort speed ranges and 30 degree direction sectors.

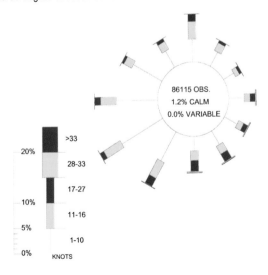

Working in the coastal and marine environment

The wind rose shown on the previous page depicts the relative frequency of wind direction on a 12-point compass. The range of mean hourly wind speed for the survey period is also indicated. In the example, south-westerly winds are dominant with wind speeds of 1–10 knots apparent for the majority of the time.

Tides

Water levels along the coast fluctuate daily, with two high and two low tides each day (in the UK). The extent and timing of tidal fluctuations depends on location. Tidal data can be obtained from Admiralty Tide Tables (see Section 2.2.3).

There are various components of the water level that need to be considered in construction. For construction works these comprise:

- storm surges
- wind set-up
- wave set-up
- seiches.

The major effect determining water level at any one instant is the astronomical tide, and this can be predicted accurately. Meteorological and seismic effects are not predictable more than a few days in advance at best, and even then the predictions are very uncertain. It is these aspects that can pose a risk to construction works.

> The ranges of astronomical tides vary greatly from site to site. Be sure to check your tide tables to see when it is safe to work in or near to the water. Spring tides (ie the highest tides) will pose more problems for your plant and workforce than neap tides (ie the lowest), but you may need the former to provide depth for barge and ship operations (eg deliveries of materials, piling etc). If in doubt, seek experienced advice (see Section 2.2.3).

Some of the components of tides and water level are partially related and relationships often arise between components of meteorological origin, such as storm surge, wind set-up, wave set-up and even seiches. There can also be some correlation between these components and astronomical tide level in shallow areas. For example, surges may propagate differently in different water depths and in response to different currents.

THE BEAUFORT SCALE

0 Sea like a mirror
1 Light air
2 Light Breeze
3 Gentle Breeze
4 Moderate Breeze
5 Fresh Breeze
6 Strong Breeze
7 Near Gale
8 Gale
9 Strong Gale
10 Storm
Violent Storm **11**
Hurricane **12**

INCREASING WIND STRENGTH

FORCE	MEAN WIND SPEED (KNOTS)
0	0
1	2
2	5
3	9
4	12
5	19
6	20
7	30
8	37
9	44
10	52
11	60
12	>60

Hurricane: The air is filled with foam and spray

Working in the coastal and marine environment 2.2

Waves

Waves probably provide the single most important hydraulic parameter in coastal engineering construction (especially when combined with high water levels). The potential impact of a wave or waves on construction works is a function of the following:

- size (height, time period, length), and direction
- likely extreme size values and direction over a period of one season, one year or more
- storm duration, persistence (ie recurrence) and sequencing.

As already mentioned, the available depth of water has a significant effect on limiting the height of waves. This depth of water is significantly increased on high tides and still further when combined with a storm surge.

Waves may be generated by winds blowing over seas immediately around the coastline. Such waves are known as "sea" and are typically relatively steep. Other waves travel from distant or old storms; these are known as "swell" and are relatively long and flat. Both can have a significant influence on construction and it should be noted that for any given wave height, swell will be more powerful and frequently more damaging.

2.2 Working in the coastal and marine environment

Waves breaking
through temporary
defences and
impacting on site
and environment
(eg through spills
of stored
materials)

 It is worth remembering that a wealth of information exists in the experience
and knowledge of the local community, particularly fishermen and yachtsmen.
Although not exact, these people may be able to provide a broad yet useful
understanding of the local environment and its processes (ie the main risks).

Currents

Except in the case of construction using caissons, the impact of tidal currents on
construction activities is generally limited, largely because they are more predictable (see
Section 2.2.3). Tidal currents, like astronomical tide levels, are foreseeable but can be
influenced by less predictable components such as wind, river discharge and surge
effects. They can be measured and described by a time-mean magnitude and direction
(and, where necessary, by spatial and turbulent variability). Information on currents is
provided in the Admiralty Charts and Tables.

Other types of currents can arise due to:

● the effects of winds blowing over areas of water setting up circulations

● breaking waves (ie alongshore currents)

● river discharges and density differences between fresh and salt water

● secondary circulation currents (eddies) generated by local bed or coastal features.

When wind and wave influences are important in current generation, it is rare for the
resulting, albeit less predictable, currents to be a governing construction consideration
when compared with the direct wind and wave effects.

Working in the coastal and marine environment

2.2.3 Estimate and plan for conditions

Make a project plan

Before going on site, the contractor should produce a plan which addresses key issues in relation to weather and sea state. This plan should take account of the following:

- The amount of time (down time) for which land-based or marine plant will be unavailable for work due to:

  - Excessive wave action causing motions which make it impractical to operate plant. For example, many items of plant are restricted to operating where wave heights do not exceed about a metre.

  - Limitations on access to the point of construction activity due to high tide levels (land based plant) or inadequate water depth (marine plant), including the effect of waves.

- Whether temporary protection would be required for the partly completed works. This can entail:

  - Phasing the work so that partial completion of more robust parts of the permanent works (ie the temporary works) protect the more vulnerable parts.

  - Physically enforcing vulnerable parts during times when storms are anticipated.

2.2 Working in the coastal and marine environment

The Met Office provides an on-line phone and fax weather forecast service (for more details contact 0845 300 0300). Designed specifically for the building and construction industry, the service provides regional or site specific weather information, essential for day-to-day operations. Bespoke forecasting should be arranged with the Met Office, with a daily fax containing a five day forecast of weather and sea state, targeted to the actual construction site (go to www.metoffice.gov.uk/construction for more details).

Your relevant environmental agency can also give information on flood warnings, covering both coastal and river flooding (www.environment-agency.gov.uk and www.sepa.org.uk). Radio weather forecasts can be obtained from the "Shipping Forecast" which is provided four times a day on BBC Radio 4 (various FM frequencies).

If you are involved in or observe a maritime emergency situation on the coast or at sea, telephone the Coastguard Agency on 999. The Coastguard Rescue Centres maintain a listening watch on Channel 16 (156.8 MHz), the marine band VHF radio distress and calling channel.

- Whether it is appropriate to completely shut down construction activity for the winter – an approach only adopted in the UK for the most exposed sites but a more frequent occurrence in other countries where seasonality is more dominant, particularly during a stormy season.

- Whether it will be necessary to design temporary works to withstand predicted extreme events, which are typically designed to withstand a one in 10 year event.

Working in the coastal and marine environment

Weather climate data

Useful data for site planning is available as follows:

- **Wind** – European Wind Atlas; BSI 6399; UK Met Office Models.

- **Wave Heights** – UK Wave Atlas; UK Meteorological Office European Model; Nomographs; Numerical Models.

- **Tides** – Admiralty Tide Tables; Tide Table Software; Surge Maps; Published Data from Research Stations.

- **Currents** – Admiralty Charts and Tables; Admiralty Pilot Books; Current Maps; Tidal Flow Models. ·

- **Weather and climate** – Information can be obtained from the UK Coastal Directory Series published by the Joint Nature Conservancy Council (JNCC).

For such project planning, the format in which wind, wave, water level and current data will be needed takes two forms:

- Normal conditions or "climate" (ie statistical presentation of the data showing the range of conditions that can be used for planning purposes to ascertain how the works could affect the environment). Ideally such information will have been prepared in advance on behalf of the client and will include information on:

    - the proportion of time different wave height thresholds are exceeded ("storms") and the variability of the length of those exceedances

    - the proportion of time different wave height thresholds are not exceeded ("calms") and the variability of the length of those non-exceedances.

- Extreme conditions (ie statistical maximum conditions).

Make a plan for today and for the rest of the week. Work out what activities can be carried out this week, given the most up-to-date weather forecast. Predictions of the weather and sea state conditions can be obtained from broadcast forecasts on the radio and internet.

2.3 Setting up and managing the site

2.3 Setting up and managing the site

2.3.1 Liaison, participation and consents

Liaison with the relevant environment agency, planning authorities, conservation agency, site neighbours and the public is essential when setting up and managing a site. The wide range of users and activities at marine sites can mean that construction projects in these locations are particularly vulnerable to complaints.

Establishing good relations with the environment agency, planning authorities and conservation agencies should include:

- identifying the extent of the liaison already undertaken at the design phase

- identifying from the specification, other contract documents, and consultation with the engineer/architect any special environmental requirements that may be required (as set out in Section 2.1)

- identifying any existing contacts

- making plans to establish working relationships with each appropriate organisation

- identifying and assigning responsibility to appropriate site staff to undertake the necessary liaison during the construction phase.

Early contact should be made with the planning liaison officer in the relevant environment agency area. If possible, arrange a site visit with all interested parties as soon as possible. In this way contacts can be made, issues identified and works can be suitably planned. Also training and induction courses should be timed to occur around the same period, so that information on habitats and other sensitive features can be passed on directly to your staff.

Checklist – consents and controls (examples only)

- **Noise** – has the local authority been asked to identify noise requirements/limits in advance of the construction phase? What are those limits?

- **Discharges** – are consents in place for any water discharges that may be required to controlled waters or a public sewer?

- **Land drainage** – have consents been obtained if required?

- **Groundwater** – Has the relevant environment agency been consulted with regard to any dewatering operations that are to be undertaken and the likely effects on groundwater reserves?

Setting up and managing the site 2.3

Checklist – consents and controls (examples only) (cont.)

- **Waste** – are procedures in place to comply with the duty of care, and have waste management licenses been obtained (if required)?

- **Traffic** – have access routes and any statutory limitations on noise and dust contained within the planning conditions for the works been identified?

- **Dredging** – have licenses been obtained for disposing of material to land or at sea?

- **Coastal construction** – has a licence been obtained for works below mean high water?

- **Environmental Management Plan** – has one been produced in response to the company EMS, if in place, and will it require implementation at the site? and

- **EAP** – has one been produced as the result of an EIA, have the actions been implemented?

Establishing good relations with site neighbours (including local residents, businesses, fisherman, the tourist industry etc) could include:

- public meetings to explain the construction of the project and its potential impacts

- regular meetings with local representatives groups

- an exhibition in a suitable local venue

- setting up liaison with local schools

- on large long term projects, a newsletter, web site, up-to-date notice boards or regular bulletins on progress, providing details of the proposed timing of disruptive activities.

Good public relations

Good public relations are vital in the drive to complete a project with the minimum disturbance to neighbours. Experience has shown that members of the public tend to complain less if they know what is happening on site. Public liaison is, therefore, particularly important if operations that are likely to cause disturbance are going to be carried out for any length of time. Try to explain the efforts that are being made to limit the impacts of operations through phasing and other control measures. Use hot-lines, newsletters, notice boards and viewing stations to encourage an understanding of the development, the costs and efforts involved, and to minimise confusion and discontent. Establishing good public relations is easier if the site personnel understand the project and its impact from the public's perspective. Training should be appropriate to the size, nature, and type of activities carried out and should emphasise the key environmental aspects and impacts of the operation, and methods for their mitigation. In particular, the need to be sensitive to local communities and aware of sensitive environmental assets must be stressed.

Considerate contractors scheme

A useful tool in demonstrating a site's environmental intentions is to work within a good practice framework; a considerate contractor scheme. These often involve adherence to a code of good practice, visits by external auditors, establishing good relations with neighbours and incentive awards for tidy sites. Considerate contractor schemes provide an ideal framework within which to manage environmental issues but do not replace an environmental management system. They are often administered by the local authority, although the Construction Industry Board has set up a nationwide scheme (see web site at www.ccscheme.org.uk).

Checklist – considerate construction

- show consideration to site neighbours and the public at large
- send letters to neighbours at the start of site work, apologise for inconvenience and provide contact information (on a notice board)
- inform neighbours if any unusual activities occur (ie early deliveries, noisy work)
- be mindful of people with sight, hearing or mobility difficulties
- monitor parking, especially on neighbouring roads and car parks
- consider ensuring that deliveries do not coincide with the rush hour
- where possible make viewing facilities available
- be responsible and respectful, lewd or derogatory language should not be tolerated and radios/music muted
- keep an incident and complaint book.

Setting up and managing the site 2.3

2.3.2 Site management, control and security

The vast majority of environmental accidents or causes of complaints stem from one or more of the following reasons:

- ignorance
- negligence
- carelessness
- vandalism.

A priority of the contractor is to ensure that site personnel understand that environmental issues must be taken seriously and that poor environmental practice will not be tolerated. Use the following checklist:

Checklist – site awareness

- Has an environmental management plan been formulated and have ideas been developed for its implementation?
- Have environmental responsibilities been defined?
- Is everyone on site aware of their responsibilities and liabilities, including sub-contractors?
- Are all environmental standards and obligations clearly defined?
- Have the standards been brought to the attention of all concerned?
- Are all established mitigation measures understood and in place?
- If training is necessary has a training programme been established?
- Are environmental awareness posters/bulletins displayed?
- Are warning signs displayed prominently on the site?
- If in place, is the company environmental policy displayed?
- If one exists, is the company environmental policy available?

Good housekeeping

Good housekeeping is an important part of good environmental practice as it helps everyone to maintain a more efficient and safer site. The site should be tidy, secure and have clear access routes that are well signposted. Particular consideration should be given to the possible effects of weather events in the coastal zone on site management and control.

2.3 # Setting up and managing the site

Checklist – housekeeping

- Segregate waste as it is produced and remove waste from the site frequently (or re-use/recycle as appropriate).
- Damp down, cover or shelter stored loose material (eg sand) to prevent it from being blown away by the wind.
- Ensure skips are emptied before they become overfilled.
- Keep the site tidy and clean (storing and locking away appropriate equipment and materials at the end of each day).
- Ensure that material and plant storage areas are properly managed.
- Keep hoardings tidy – repair them and repaint them when necessary, remove any fly posting.
- Frequently brush clean the wheel washing facilities.
- Do not leave plant unattended in public areas or in the vicinity of the tidal zone.

General site appearance is important. When planning the site layout, all offices and equipment should be sited to minimise visual intrusion. In coastal areas, consideration must be given to minimising impact, both on neighbours and on recreational users.

Site Security

Site security is an important component of good environmental management. Vandals often cause damage that harms the environment, by:

- opening taps on tanks containing fuel
- tipping out other liquids from drums and containers
- smashing/stealing raw materials
- playing on plant
- spraying graffiti or flyposting on site hoardings
- destroying works in progress.

 Contractors can be liable for environmental damage caused by vandals if they have not made reasonable attempts to guard against it. A contractor's liability increases if vandals have already struck at a site.

Help reduce vandalism by securing the site, and moving valuable items and those prone to theft from public view. Store these items in locked containers or a storage area.

Setting up and managing the site

Although emergency equipment can be particularly vulnerable, it should not be locked away when the site is active as daily checks are required to check its usability.

Suggested security measures include:

- Where possible, secure the site boundary using perimeter fencing and high quality locks on gates. Various types of fencing are available and each has its own advantages and drawbacks. For example, solid barriers (eg hoardings), are more difficult to scale than chain-link fences and prevent casual surveillance by prospective thieves. However, they also provide cover for thieves and vandals once they are on site.

Lockable fuel dispenser to prevent vandalism

- Avoid stacking materials against the site boundary/fence, as this can provide an opportunity for vandals and thieves to scale it.

- Within the site, ensure that materials that are potentially hazardous to the environment are well secured. It is important to lock fuel outlets when not in use.

- Secure plant to prevent vandalism.

- Immobilise plant and equipment overnight.

- Install deterrents such as lights, warning notices, 24-hour security guards (where appropriate) and alarm systems.

- Control the movement of people on and off the site: use site passes or swipe cards.

- Position the site manager's office to give a good view of the site.

- If the site is large or at high risk from trespassers, consider installing CCTV cameras.

- Inform local police about the site and seek their advice on security.

2.3 Setting up and managing the site

Pollutants

It is essential that equipment, fuel and materials are secured to prevent them entering water courses; environmental damage and prosecution could result and the recovery of materials can be costly. This is covered further in Chapters 3.1, 3.5, 4.16 and 4.17.

2.3.3 Working hours; noise and lighting

Site working hours can create considerable concern and annoyance among neighbours, in particular due to noise and light pollution.

Noise

Coastal sites can be more susceptible to risks associated with noise restrictions due to the inherent nature of the works (eg rock unloading, the use of large moving plant and piling works), the fact that water is acoustically "hard" (ie sound waves move over water rather than penetrate), and also due to the often close proximity of neighbours (especially tourists in the summer).

Conflict can arise due to the need to maximise the utilisation of marine plant and the need to optimise the tidal windows available. This is often against accepted working hour standards and can lead to a high level of complaint. The potential effects of noise in coastal locations can also be exaggerated by the propagation of noise over water to potential receptors and by the limited applicability of some noise control measures at the coast, such as bunds.

On some projects, the working hours for noisy operations are defined by the local authority and stipulated within the contract document, for example through Section 60 or 61 notices. There may be opportunities for extending working hours in consultation with the local authority or the client. Although extensions to working hours may be crucial to the programme (particularly on projects that require tidal working), their effect on neighbours should be carefully considered – try to stick to sociable working hours as far as practicable. When extended working is necessary, it is important to inform neighbours in advance of the reasons for the work and its duration.

Time activities within the allowable day carefully. For example, in the same way that it is advisable to schedule deliveries outside the rush hour, other intrusive activities can be scheduled at less sensitive times. To understand the constraints, which will vary from site to site, it is important to establish the patterns of neighbours (including the tourist industry and business) and the public.

Timing of activities

- plan works well in advance, identify the issues, discuss and solve them before going on site

- in remote locations, night-time noise may be more acceptable than day-time noise, if there are no residential areas and there is high recreational use of the area during the day. However, be aware that night time noise may be unacceptable in environmentally sensitive locations (eg breeding season)

- avoid noisy activities during school hours (if applicable)

- local restaurants appreciate less disturbance over lunch time

- establish whether local business or the tourist industry require quieter periods during the day

- determine whether weekend or night-time working is especially sensitive (consider tourist activities as well as residents)

- establish whether there are particularly sensitive receptors near the site

- understand the seasonal requirements of wildlife (including breeding birds), tourism and recreation.

Lighting

Lighting is essential for many coastal activities, not only as a deterrent to vandals but also to maximise working hours, for the use of machinery, and to provide suitable working conditions. However light can be a source of annoyance to local residents so it is essential to keep site lighting at the minimum brightness necessary for adequate security and safety. Locate and direct the lighting so that it does not intrude on any properties nearby and remember that high levels of lighting waste energy and money. Consider the use of infra-red lighting for security.

2.3 Setting up and managing the site

2.3.4 Managing materials

Improving the delivery and management of materials and components reduces materials wastage and increases site efficiency. The environmental benefits of reducing wastage include minimising resource use and the amount of waste sent for disposal. Where site personnel follow established procedures for managing materials and components there will be fewer incidents of spillage and contamination arising from incorrect storage or handling, and less damage to materials and components. This means less wastage of raw materials and, hence, saving money.

Storage

A combination of central storage and workplace storage is typically used on site. The balance between them depends on the site and the works in progress. It is important to manage storage areas well because they set an example for the site.

Checklist – storage of materials

- ensure that the materials suppliers' instructions on storage and delivery are being followed

- store materials that are valuable or attractive to thieves in a secure area

- take care not to store fragile equipment in site offices that may be subject to tidal flooding (including maximum spring tides)

- do not store material or position offices on or near to cliffs or slopes that may be unstable

- consider storing materials in a central storage area away from sensitive receptors such as watercourses

- store materials away from waste storage containers and from vehicle movements that could cause accidental damage

- secure lightweight materials to protect them from wind damage or loss

- take special care over the storage of materials that are potentially polluting

- ensure that when storing materials the effects of extreme weather in the coastal zone is considered and appropriate action taken

- make sure that all appropriate emergency response equipment is located near to the stored material and that staff know how to use it.

Setting up and managing the site 2.3

Handling

There are many methods for moving materials around the site. Options include cranes, trucks, fork lifts and even manual handling. Ensure that the suppliers' instructions on handling their materials are followed to minimise damage to materials and injury to site personnel. Particular care should be taken when moving potentially polluting materials around the site.

Ordering and receiving materials

- order the right quantity and quality

- if materials arrive at the time when they are needed, this reduces the length of time materials have to be stored on site and, therefore, reduces the potential for damage, pollution and theft to occur

- consider whether large volumes of potentially polluting materials need to be stored on the site. Can the material be delivered to site in quantities that can be used on the day of delivery?

- can potentially polluting materials be eliminated from the construction process altogether or could relevant processes be undertaken elsewhere (ie at a more suitable site)?

- when ordering, find out in what form the materials will be delivered in, so that appropriate unloading plant can be arranged

- after placing an order, check the arrangements for handling and storing the materials as soon as they arrive on site

- always make sure that deliveries are received by a member of site personnel who is able to supervise the delivery, carry out a quality inspection and ensure that the materials are unloaded to the appropriate place

- make sure that all delivery drivers and site staff are aware of these conditions.

Waste minimisation

Construction waste originates from three main sources: earthworks and excavation; demolition; and general construction. It is estimated that some 70 million tonnes of construction and demolition waste arise annually in the UK. The creation of waste on your site creates a number of problems, namely:

- the costs incurred in removing the waste

- the costs incurred for the safe disposal of the waste (ie landfill tax)

- the increasing need for waste disposal sites around the UK

- the misuse of potentially valuable or marketable products.

2.3 Setting up and managing the site

To lessen the effects of these issues on industry, the practice of waste minimisation has been widely adopted. Waste minimisation helps businesses to save money through reductions in wastage and also helps to improve market image through increased awareness of sustainable development issues.

> Did you know that 60–80% of materials on-site can be re-used, including: woods, metals, aggregates, glass, plastics, slate, tiles and cardboard?

The key elements of waste minimisation are as follows:

- reuse of materials or use of recycled materials

- appropriate materials and dimensions, prefabrication

- efficient ordering of materials (see above)

- materials handling and storage (see above)

- efficient waste management – segregation

- efficient waste management – auditing.

The above issues and elements are covered in more detail in Chapter 3.1.4.

Key guidance

- *Demonstrating waste minimisation benefits in construction*, CIRIA, C536, 2001.

- *Managing materials and components on site*, CIRIA, SP146, 1998.

CIRIA has launched an internet register of construction waste recycling facilities located within Great Britain (see the CIRIA website www.ciria.org.uk). This register will encourage better disposal of construction and demolition wastes and will help companies to source recycled products.

2.3.5 Traffic and access routes

It is important to manage site traffic, because it can cause delays to local traffic and create a safety hazard both on and off site. People living and working near the site are often annoyed by emissions, noise and the visual intrusion of queuing vehicles. An organised site with well-managed traffic activities can provide a positive perspective to local residents.

Access routes

The use of public roads for site access may be restricted (ie within the planning consent). Such restrictions may include weight and width controls, parking controls, steps to minimise pedestrian conflict and low-headroom access routes. Even if these aspects are covered within the contract, consult the local police and the local authority fully to address potential traffic issues and agree on a workable site access that does not compromise public safety. Plans may be required to identify each access point, the agreed route to the nearest main road, and the routes to be used by lorries to access the road network. Wherever possible, arrange the access so that lorries enter and exit the site in a forwards direction.

When undertaking certain coastal projects, delivery of materials may be possible by sea and should be investigated because of the clear advantages of minimising traffic disruption. However, there is a risk that the sea conditions will disrupt deliveries.

 Send a site map to your suppliers, showing them where you wish them to access the site and how to get there.

Managing site traffic

Plan the timing of deliveries to avoid vehicles waiting. Where several deliveries are likely to take place over a short period, designate queuing areas. In summer avoid queuing outside buildings, as windows will most likely be open, and try to avoid vehicles reducing the amenity and recreation value of surroundings areas. In urban areas it may be best to allocate a waiting area some distance from site and call in deliveries when access to the site is clear.

Site personnel car traffic often annoys the public. Arrange designated parking areas, ensure that staff do not park in unsuitable areas and that restrictions are complied with. Consider implementing a park-and-ride or car-share scheme. Try not to monopolise public car parking areas, especially those used during the summer by high numbers of visitors to the area.

Sometimes construction sites are blamed for disturbance caused by vehicles that are not associated with the site. To avoid this it may be helpful if site vehicles display some visible identifying marks. While this may not be appropriate for individual deliveries it can be done for the main contractor's vehicles and for regular delivery vehicles.

2.3 Setting up and managing the site

Checklist – managing site traffic

- when ordering deliveries, ensure that all drivers are aware of traffic restrictions at and around the site
- arrange deliveries to site so that vehicles can go straight in without having to queue outside the site boundary
- store materials as close to where they are needed as possible
- instruct drivers to switch off engines when vehicles are waiting
- consider the use of in-cab communication systems to maintain control over lorry movements
- load and unload vehicles off the highway, wherever possible;
- plan parking for site personnel's vehicles
- consider getting regular site vehicles to display identification.

2.3.6 Emergency actions and remediation

The nature of coastal and marine sites requires that emergency action plans are put in place to deal with potential pollution incidents before setting up the site. It is essential that consideration is given to controlling and containing solid and liquids pollutants along with detailed action plans for dealing with emergencies. In some situations, for example oils and lubricants especially on or in close proximity to water, the purchase of a range of specialist equipment to tackle spills may be required. Section 3.5.5 covers this area in detail.

If land or water become contaminated through the spillage of oils, lubricants or other substances, remediation will be required. This will take place after the initial clean up and will require advice from the relevant environmental agency and/or specialist consultants.

Key guidance

- Pollution incident response planning, Pollution Prevention Guidance Note 21, Environment Agency, SEPA, Environment and Heritage Service.

Setting up and managing the site

(2.3)

2.3.7 Pollution avoidance

It is essential that pollution avoidance strategies are used when working in coastal locations.

Checklist – pollution avoidance

- **Wastewater control** – ensure that all waste water produced on site is disposed of appropriately and cannot enter controlled waters.

- **Waste management** – ensure that appropriate containers are available for the collection and disposal of all wastes.

- **Air pollution control** – ensure that equipment is serviced and managed to minimise air pollution.

- **Noise control** – ensure that plans are in place to mitigate noise levels from any major noise sources to keep them within acceptable limits.

- **Light control** – ensure that lighting is correctly set up and focused to avoid causing pollution through 'light spill'.

- **Spillage control** – ensure that all liquids are appropriately stored to prevent spillage.

2.3.8 Managing monitoring and mitigation equipment

In order to meet the requirements of existing consents it may be necessary to have a range of monitoring and mitigation equipment on site. This could include noise meters and flow meters for monitoring volumes of discharges. Mitigation equipment could include oil spill kits, screens to trap dust, and screens/bunds to reduce noise. To remain effective, all equipment will need to be managed. Monitoring equipment will require regular servicing, and possibly calibration (and certificate), by a competent authority. To avoid complaints and ensure compliance with consents, mitigation equipment should also be regularly checked. Spill kits, and other emergency "first aid" kit, should be checked on a daily basis.

> ⚠️ On-site accident and emergency equipment, such as spill kits, should be kept in an easily accessed location. Relevant trained staff should know of its location and how to use the equipment.

2.3 Setting up and managing the site

2.3.9 Site clearance/abandonment

This is a phase of the works that can receive little attention but it can cause most problems. In clearing the site it is vital that wastes are managed in accordance with relevant regulations. Normally, on completion of the works, the contractor is required to clear away and remove from the site all plant, surplus materials, rubbish and temporary works. The whole of the site and works should be left clean – until then the project is unfinished.

It is likely that the project's planning permission and waste management licence (if granted), will have conditions attached. It is usual for these conditions to address post-construction landscaping and reinstatement issues and it is a legal requirement to comply with them.

In clearing the site, options for the salvage, re-use and recycling of materials should be considered (see Managing Materials 2.3.4 and Waste Issues 3.1.4). Finally, any disposal of waste should be carried out with regard to the Duty of Care and relevant legislation and policies on waste.

3 Environmental issues

3.1 Waste (storage and disposal)

3.1.1 Waste management

What is waste?

Problems often arise with waste because there is confusion as to what waste actually is. Legally, waste is defined as "any substances or objects which the holder discards, intends to discard, or is required to discard". Consequently, materials that people do not normally regard as a waste may fall under this definition, for example excavated spoil. If in doubt seek advice from the appropriate environment agency. Be aware that there are many different types of waste and these need to be treated differently.

Definitions of different types of waste

Inactive waste – materials that do not undergo significant physical, chemical or biological reactions or cause environmental pollution when deposited at a landfill under normal conditions. These include uncontaminated sediments, soils and rocks, ceramics, concrete, masonry, brick rubble and minerals.

Active wastes – those that are not inactive wastes. They include acids, pesticides, wood preservative, oily sludges, batteries, waste oils, asbestos, timber, plastics, alkaline solutions and bitumen. Some active wastes may also be special wastes. Active waste is subject to a higher rate of landfill tax than inactive waste.

Special wastes – those that are deemed to be dangerous to life; they may be corrosive, reactive, oxidising, carcinogenic or flammable. Some of the more common special wastes include acids, alkaline solutions, oily sludges, waste oils and wood preservatives. The criteria to be used to determine whether a waste is special is specified in the Special Waste Regulations (1996) and in the Environment Agency Guide to the Special Waste Regulations 1996 (as amended), November 2001.

3.1.2 Fines and costs

Impacts from poor waste management are wide ranging. As well as financial costs and likely damage to the environment (eg spills, odours), there is also the potential for knock-on effects for the project as a whole (including delays in the construction programme). In addition, court fines are increasing, as are clean-up and recovery costs. However, careful waste management can prevent these needless financial and time costs.

> Following illegal deposition of wastes, consisting of soil and hardcore onto the floodplain of the River Wey, and failure to remove the materials, the contractor was sentenced to two months imprisonment for each of three related offences.

3.1.3 The main risks

Effective waste management should be an integral part of any construction project. There are three main reasons for considering waste management early on in a project:

1. **Compliance with legislation** – Sites must comply with legislation concerning the storage, handling, transport and disposal of waste. Fines for non-compliance are increasing.

2. **Damage to the environment** – The UK construction and demolition industry generated over 70 million tonnes of waste (including excavation spoil) in 1999. This is about four times the rate of household waste per person. There are direct environmental impacts associated with dealing with these wastes, such as finding space for landfill. There are also indirect impacts, including noise and traffic emissions from haulage, that would not arise if the waste were not produced.

3. **Impact on project programme and budget** – The true cost of waste includes:

   - the purchase price of materials that are being wasted (including the fees imposed by Aggregates Tax)
   - the cost of transporting, handling and storing those materials
   - the cost of handling, storing and transporting the waste
   - the cost of disposing of the waste, including landfill tax. In 2002, the standard rate of landfill tax was at £13 per tonne (increasing to £15 in 2004/5) for active waste and £2 per tonne for inactive waste
   - the cost of the time spent managing the waste
   - the loss of income from not salvaging the wasted materials.

Handling waste inefficiently will cost time, money and effort. It may also lead to environmental pollution (eg spillage).

> The Landfill Tax Regulations (1996) have encouraged producers to look for alternative uses for construction waste and the amounts landfilled have reduced since the tax was introduced. The new Aggregates Tax may also provide an incentive for more recycling and minimisation of waste, through discouraging demand for virgin aggregates.

When working in the coastal or marine environment the above is especially important as particular consideration has to be given to, and methods of working must allow for, preventing wastes from entering the water. Likewise, consideration must be given to recovery operations should wastes actually enter the water.

3.1.4 Reducing waste

Waste problems can be avoided by successful on-site management, initiated by an efficient waste minimisation strategy (introduced in Section 2.3.4). To manage wastes effectively, focus on:

- the amount of materials that are wasted
- the way in which wastes are handled and stored
- the amount of wastes that can be reclaimed
- the method of disposal of wastes.

The site manager should allocate responsibility for these issues to nominated individuals. On larger sites it may be appropriate to designate one person as the site waste manager.

Adopt the 4 "R" Strategy
REDUCE
RECLAIM
REUSE
RECYCLE

The above waste hierarchy has been established to help industry develop strategies for waste minimisation. Do you think about the above before reaching the "Disposal" option?

Use the box below to focus on how materials are ordered, delivered, stored and handled on-site, in order to establish how wastage can be reduced.

Reducing wastage of material	
Ordering – try to: ● order exact quantities required ● order required lengths ● order delivery at the required time.	Delivery – try to: ● prevent damage during unloading ● deliver to a suitable location on-site ● accept only deliveries with correct specifications and quantities.
Storage – try to: ● use products before the end of their shelf life ● avoid damage or contamination ● avoid loss, theft and vandalism.	Handling – try to: ● ensure correct handling to avoid damage ● ensure that the correct materials are delivered to the workplace.
ALWAYS RE-USE WASTE MATERIAL WHERE POSSIBLE!	

To manage wastes efficiently it is important to allocate sufficient space and resources in advance. Developing a waste management strategy requires knowledge of the types and quantities of waste likely to be generated on-site. This information may be obtained by monitoring wastes on-site or by drawing on previous experience.

Monitoring wastes on-site

The site manager should arrange for waste audits to be carried out at regular intervals to look at:

- the quantities of raw material wastage
- the quantities of each type of waste generated
- the way in which wastes are being handled and stored
- the costs of disposal for different types of wastes.

It may be useful to undertake a small number of "spot checks" on your waste carriers. For example, check that the waste does actually arrive at the agreed licensed destination. You can also check the transit time of the carrier (ie if it returns to the site without sufficient time having elapsed for it to have reached the licensed destination). These checks are very important, as the waste producer is legally responsible for making certain that the material to be disposed of is done so correctly.

Checklist – transportation of wastes (Duty of Care)

- Check that there is a copy of the carrier's registration document on-site and that it is still valid. This can be checked with the relevant environment agencies.
- The waste carrier must be authorised to carry the type of waste for disposal.
- The transfer notes should be completed in full and contain an accurate description of the waste.
- Keep copies of all transfer notes of waste sent off-site.

Storage

All wastes must be stored in designated areas that are isolated from surface water drains, open water and are bunded to contain any spillage. Waste compactors should be covered to prevent the build up of contaminated rainwater, and drained to the foul sewer to prevent polluting liquid from entering surface water drains or the sea/watercourse. Under some circumstances, for example if storing and treating material from a contaminated site, a Waste Management Licence may be required (see Section 3.1.6).

Skips must be covered to prevent dust and litter from being blown out and rainwater entering. Where possible, separate skips should be provided so that wastes can be segregated for recycling or to prevent cross contamination. All special wastes must be put in sealed double bags and segregated from other waste streams. Under current legislation, if special waste contaminates a skip, the whole skip becomes special waste. It is important that all waste containers are clearly labelled with their contents and are not allowed to accumulate (ie to be stock-piled).

The storage of non-waste materials is detailed in Section 2.3.4 but should not be confused with the storage of waste products.

Checklist – storage of wastes

- segregate different types of waste as they are generated
- mark waste containers clearly with their intended contents – consider colour coding
- use containers suitable for their contents – check their condition
- minimise the risk of accidental spillage or leaks – containers should be placed in impervious bunded areas
- ensure that wastes cannot be blown or washed away – containers must be securely covered.

3.1.5 Recognising issues and taking action

The site manager should arrange for regular reviews of waste management procedures, with specific regard to:

- the amount of raw material wastage
- the storing and handling of waste
- the amount of waste going to landfill
- the waste minimisation strategy, if adopted, and its success
- following the regulations/guidance on waste transport and disposal.

If any issues are discovered, the site manager is responsible for ensuring that corrective action is taken. Appropriate measures and actions are listed above.

3.1.6 Main legislation and key references

Environmental Protection Act 1990

In England, Wales and Scotland, Part II of the Environmental Protection Act provides the main controls for waste management, including the introduction of a "duty of care" on all those who produce or keep waste to require them to prevent the escape of waste, ensure proper disposal and ensure transfer to a registered carrier with a proper transfer note. Refer to the Environmental Protection (Duty of Care) Regulations (1991) for more information.

Special Waste Regulations 1996

These regulations apply if special wastes are produced on-site. Special Waste is regulated in England, Scotland and Wales by the Special Waste Regulations 1996 (and amendments). Special waste includes hazardous and toxic wastes, such as solvents, thinners, waste oils, paints, metal sludges, and chemicals.

Carriage of Dangerous Goods by Road Regulations 1996 and the Carriage of Dangerous Goods by Rail Regulations 1996

In the UK, these regulations require that special wastes are considered dangerous and include requirements that:

- suitable vehicles are used for transport
- emergency instructions, in writing, are available during transport
- appropriate care is taken during loading, storage and unloading.

Waste Management Licensing Regulations 1994

In the UK, these regulations (and amendments) make it an offence to:

- treat, keep or dispose of controlled waste in a manner likely to cause pollution of the environment or harm to human health
- treat, keep or dispose of, or to knowingly cause or permit controlled waste to be treated, kept or disposed of except under, and in accordance with, a waste management licence.

Consequently, if surplus excavated or demolition materials are to be used in the construction works, it may be necessary to obtain a waste management licence for the site. The advice of the relevant environment agency should be sought in each case.

Food and Environment Protection Act 1985

The relevant Government Environment Departments in the UK (the licensing authority) have a statutory duty to control the deposit of articles or materials in the sea and/or in tidal waters. The Act requires that a licence be obtained from the relevant Department in order that the disposal of waste (ie excavated materials), can be undertaken. Licences are also required for the placement of structures and materials at sea or in tidal waters (below Mean High Water Springs). This includes materials used during construction (eg for new harbours, offshore structures etc), and for "soft engineering" purposes (eg beach nourishment, groynes etc).

Key guidance – waste

- *Waste management – the Duty of Care*, Code of Practice, HMSO

- *Demonstrating waste minimisation benefits in construction*, CIRIA C536, 2001

- *The reclaimed and recycled materials handbook*, CIRIA C513, 1999

- *Managing materials and components on-site*, CIRIA SP146, 1998

- *Use of industrial by-products in road construction – water quality effects*, CIRIA R167, 1998

- *Waste minimisation in construction – site guide*, CIRIA, SP133, 1997
  Guidance on the disposal of dredged material to land, CIRIA, R157, 1996

- Environment Agency, SEPA and Environment and Heritage Service, Pollution Prevention Guidelines (PPG):

  - PPG 6, Working at Construction and Demolition Sites

  - PPG 8, Safe storage and disposal of used oils

  - PPG 23, Maintenance of structures over water

- Environment Agency, SEPA and Environment and Heritage Service, A Guide to the Special Waste Regulations 1996 (as amended), version 2, November 2001;

- Envirowise Reference Notes:

  - 163 – Determining if Material is Hazardous/Special Waste

  - 164 – Special Waste Regulations.

3.2 Noise and Vibration

3.2.1 The importance of noise and vibration

Noise

Noise can have wide ranging effects during construction on the coast and in marine areas. Whilst most impacts relate to hazards to workers or annoyance caused to neighbours (as covered in C502), additional effects can occur to marine and coastal birds, fisheries and other aquatic life, such as seals, whales and dolphins. If complaints are received and investigated by your local authority or conservation agency, it will lead to delays to your construction programme and subsequent cost increases.

Vibration

At high levels and over long periods of time, vibration from construction activities (ie piling, demolition, haulage), can cause damage to buildings and sensitive equipment – computers for example. Lower levels can cause nuisance to local residents and businesses, but the level of annoyance will depend on the type of activity and the intensity of the vibration. Vibration may also affect archaeological sites, geological features and directly disturb wildlife. The level at which disturbance occurs will be highly site-specific.

3.2.2 Fines and costs

Noise

Fines and costs are likely to result from the creation of excessive noise affecting the local community and/or wildlife. Fines are likely to be a last resort but can occur due to action taken by the local authority or community (eg a civil action). Costs may also arise from noise mitigation schemes that have to be put into place, altered construction programmes due to limits on working patterns (such as timing restrictions, see Section 2.3.3) and compensation paid to affected parties.

> In 1996/1997 local authorities received over 8000 noise complaints concerning construction activities and served 669 notices requiring action to reduce noise.

Vibration

There are no specific guidelines setting standards for ground-borne vibrations and, as such, no local authority guidance or specifications exist. However, where damage is caused to property or structures and remedial works could be required, civil suits can be taken. Furthermore, if the structure is a listed building or Scheduled Monument, additional fines or costs may be incurred.

3.2 Noise and vibration

3.2.3 The main risks

Noise

Noise on-site may occur from a range of construction activities. The most likely source of problems is piling, which can be the loudest activity on-site. However, other activities such as excavation and generator and equipment use, may well provide a source of complaint, particularly during sensitive periods such as at night or on Bank Holidays.

Noise management may therefore be required so as not to affect local residents and/or wildlife. It is essential to avoid action by local authorities, or civil actions, as these could prove to be costly through fines and delays.

When working on construction projects on the coast or at sea, it is important to remember that noise propagation paths will be affected. Water will allow the noise to travel over greater distances than would otherwise be the case. This must be considered when assessing the potential effects of noise on marine fauna and adjacent communities (eg on the opposite bank of an estuary).

> The extent to which seismic disturbance affects marine wildlife is not well known due to the limited research carried out to date. Seismic surveys at sea do not necessarily constitute a threat to marine wildlife, if care is taken to avoid situations which could potentially harm the animals.
>
> Any company wishing to carry out a seismic survey must apply for consent from the Department of Trade and Industry (DTI). The Joint Nature Conservation Committee (JNCC) is consulted on whether consent should be granted for each individual seismic survey. If a consent is granted, a standard condition is that the JNCC "Guidelines for minimising acoustic disturbance to marine mammals from seismic surveys" are followed. Further information from the Senior Offshore Advisor, JNCC, Aberdeen (01224 655716).

Vibration

Sustained high levels of vibration can cause damage to nearby structures, they can also cause annoyance, and result in high local concern (ie accusations of causing damage). Damage is more likely if there are structures very close to the source of the vibration, where ground conditions are such that the transmission of vibrations is high, or where water levels are high which allows vibrations to travel further.

3.2.4 Limiting the impact of noise and vibration

Noise

Noise limits and restrictions on working times or areas (see Section 2.3.3) may be specified by the local planning authority, and should be identified within the clients' conditions of contract. Therefore, the contractor should ensure that all equipment and working methods conform to these standards and restrictions. This may include the use of specific equipment (ie silencers), no or restricted working during weekends or evenings, etc. Most importantly, all site-staff should be made aware of the conditions and the reasons for them.

Contractors are advised to manage noise in a pro-active way and to anticipate and manage potential sources of noise before they occur. After complying with contractual noise limits, the priority should be to avoid causing conflict with the local community and businesses, including fishermen. This should maintain good public relations and reduce the risk of constraints being placed on working practices through the imposition of statutory notices by the local authority.

> When working in or next to a sensitive natural or built environment, the use of screening such as baffle boards will help to limit the impact of noise. Other measures such as limiting staff access to the crest of embankments, restricting radios and loud music, and the provision of adequate levels of awareness to personnel will also help.

There are three factors that influence noise levels at a given site:

1. Site management and construction methods.

2. Plant type and characteristics.

3. Screening.

Of the above, the greatest benefits can be achieved by simply employing good practice methods (ie timing, public awareness etc). Further reductions can be made by directing attention to specific equipment or methods.

In planning the approach to noise reduction on a project, the benefits to be gained from each factor should be weighed against the cost of implementation. In some situations there may be only one solution. BS 5228 (see Section 3.2.6) shows how to work out the predicted noise from construction operations based on the methods, plant and screening used.

3.2 Noise and vibration

The following gives guidance on what to consider in developing your approach.

Site management and construction method (ie timing, duration and phasing)

The general operation of the site needs to be addressed in order to control noise. It is not only loud noises that cause complaint but also anti-social activity and irregular or tonal noises, such as vehicle reversing warnings. Site managers should also consider other reasons for complaint including shouting, bad language, radios, unnecessary revving of engines or idling, and out of hours deliveries.

Some of the construction activities that cause the greatest problems are: piling (particularly by diesel hammer), "breaking out" with pneumatic tools, falling ball demolition, using a bucket dredger, earthmoving, concrete pours and maintenance works. In the aquatic environment, the use of blasting during construction can also result in extremely high levels of noise. Calculating noise levels for actual construction noise involves combining the cumulative effects of many different items of plant (see CIRIA PR70 *How much noise do you make? A guide to assessing and managing noise on construction sites* for examples of how this is done).

Plant

Noise levels from individual items of plant can vary considerably depending on how they are configured and used. Therefore, careful selection of plant and equipment is essential where noise is important. BS 5228 provides guidance on noise levels from construction and from typical plant with and without sound control measures. To minimise the noise from the plant on your site, observe the following rules:

● use only plant conforming with the relevant standards and directives on emissions

● older plant, although still legal to use, may not have such identification. As it is likelier to be noisier than modern plant, avoid using it in noise sensitive areas

● fit silencers to all vehicles and plant.

Reducing noise levels

Detailed noise control methods for plant, including screening methods, increasing community tolerance, and noise monitoring are covered in CIRIA C502. Examples include:

● adopting silenced piling techniques

● adhering to the following good practice guidelines:

  – BS5228 (1997) *Noise and Vibration control on construction and open sites*; Part 1 – Code of Practice for basic information and procedures for noise and vibration control. Also, Part 4 (1992) – Noise and vibration control applicable to piling operations

  – Construction (Design Management) Regulations 1994

  – Health and Safety Executive Regulation/Guidance.

- fitting construction plant, such as generators and pumps, with appropriate silencers and acoustic enclosures and/or hoods (where appropriate) in order to minimise the effects of noise

- siting stationary noise sources (eg generators), as far as possible from sensitive noise receptors.

Vibration

Significant effects of the building works, such as the effects of vibration on nearby properties and structures should have been addressed at the design phase.

If this has not been undertaken at the design stage, an assessment of the risks to structures from ground-borne vibrations should be undertaken. In general the greatest indicator of risk are the proximity of structures to the activities and whether significant vibration induced activities are to occur (eg piling). If there are structures close to the works and high level vibration inducing activities, specialists should be brought in to assess the risk and identify measures to minimise vibration and monitoring methods.

Measures to minimise vibration

The following generic measures reduce the magnitude and/or frequency of vibration caused by particular site works, and could be used to avoid excess vibration and hence risk to nearby structures (see C502 for further detail):

- use of vibrating machinery rather than piling or driving machinery to significantly minimise the levels of vibration

- use of machinery/equipment that creates high frequency vibration rather than low frequency vibrations. High frequency vibrations travel less distance than low frequency. Check with manufacturers for the vibration frequency emitted by equipment

- use heavy bases rather than light bases, as they minimise the induced vibration levels

- if working in an area of fluctuating ground water levels (ie adjacent to coastal areas), undertake activity during low tide when the ground water levels are lower.

3.2 Noise and vibration

3.2.5 Recognising problems and taking action

Actions in areas with or adjacent to sensitive noise receptors

For dealing with complaints from the local community and the local authority (ie the environmental health officer), it is suggested that a community relations officer is appointed to ensure that the construction work is carried out correctly. As well as informing local residents of expected noisy periods in the construction schedule, potential complaints can be spotted at an early stage so that mitigation measures can be put in place to avoid formal action being taken. A number of mitigation measures are identified in the good practice table below.

Good practice – works near to sensitive noise receptors

- Mitigation for noise disturbance is often undertaken in the form of scheduling and programming noisy activities to avoid "sleep disturbance", rather than stating critical noise limits. The exception being where extremely sensitive receptors are present (eg hospitals and schools, designated sites of nature conservation importance).

- Consult the Local Council's Environmental Health Department should work have to be undertaken outside agreed construction hours.

- Have a responsible approach to work carried out on-site in order that noise is reduced to practicable levels.

- Send letters to sensitive residences giving them details of the construction work.

- Publish timings of noisy works in the local newspaper.

- Provide details of works on posters or on information notice boards on-site.

Actions in areas of sensitive marine fauna

- For dredging, one of the most appropriate and initial actions to reduce noise is the choice of equipment. Although this would be determined to an extent by the substrate type, where noise sensitive receptors are present close to the dredge area, the use of cutter suction dredgers would produce the least noise, particularly with respect to acoustic wave energy in the aquatic environment.

- Avoid specific seasonal periods (eg mating season or salmon runs), particularly if activities such as blasting are to be undertaken. These sorts of activity should avoid seasons when sensitive receptors (identified in fisheries and nature conservation sections), are present in large numbers, or at their most sensitive, for example when mating/pupping (in the case of seals).

CIRIA Publication C584

- Operational procedures in the marine environment can be adjusted for minimal disturbance. For example, when blasting, undertake during the day but not at sunrise or sunset. Use visual surveys to ensure sensitive species (eg mammals) are not close to the blast area (eg 1 km). Another operational method can include the ramp-up of levels, where noise is slowly increased to encourage species to move away from the source area prior to significant noise emissions. Small blasts followed by the larger operational blasts, and intermittent blasts rather than continuous to minimise the overall noise energy.

- The potential effects of noise and vibration on fisheries are summarised in Section 3.7.3 but, in brief, it may be necessary to assess fisheries for signs of fish mortality and distress, being especially aware of the effects that can occur to juvenile fish and shellfish. Any mitigation measures should be discussed with the local fisheries inspector, as appropriate.

See Section 2.3.3 for further detail on good practice with regard to noise and the timing of works.

Vibration

By undertaking a risk assessment, the likelihood of vibration damage to properties can be ascertained. If damage is not thought to be likely, as a precaution it is still recommended that nearby structures be monitored to determine levels of vibration experienced, and surveyed prior to the works commencing and during and after the work is completed. The owners (or guardians) of the structures that could be at risk should be consulted prior to construction so that the risks can be explained, and an agreed system of monitoring and surveying determined.

Monitoring

Monitoring should be undertaken by experienced specialists and should include the outside of the structure to assess the risk of damage, and inside the structure if there is a potential for nuisance (ie if residential or commercial properties are nearby). The measured levels can be compared against those predicted by the specialist risk assessment, and/or by the standards identified in BRE Digest 353.

Surveying

Where a possible risk of damage to structures may arise, it is not uncommon for surveys of the structure (using measurements of cracks, video, photography, etc), to be undertaken before work starts, during periods of intense vibration inducing activity, and after the construction period.

3.2.6 Main legislation and key references

Control of Pollution Act 1974 (COPA)

In England, Wales and Scotland, a local authority can control noise from construction sites by serving a Section 60 notice, which defines what plant and machinery may be used, the working hours and noise levels. A developer may apply for prior consent for construction works through Section 61. It is a defence against any prosecution under Section 60 to have a Section 61 consent in place, provided that the developer is complying with the terms and conditions of that consent. It is also a defence, whether or not a Section 61 consent exists, to demonstrate that best practicable means are being used to minimise noise emissions. "Best practicable means" (BPM) is defined in Section 72 as having regard to, among other things, local conditions and circumstances, the current state of technical knowledge and reasonable cost. The local authority can also designate noise abatement zones, in which specified types of development may not exceed specified noise levels. Since either Section 60 or Section 61 procedures may be appropriate, designated site staff should be familiar with the requirements of each.

In Northern Ireland, similar provisions are made to Section 60/61 in the Pollution Control and Local Government (Northern Ireland) Order 1978.

Noise at Work Regulations 1989

This is a statutory legal document that details provision for the protection of people's hearing while in the workplace (England, Wales and Scotland only). Various levels of acoustic exposure are specified which, when exceeded, determine the level of protection required. Failure to comply with the specifications may lead to prosecution under the Health and Safety Regulations.

Environmental Protection Act 1990

In England, Wales and Scotland under this Act, the local authority and private individuals can instigate proceedings to serve or obtain an abatement order for noise that is considered to constitute a nuisance. In Part III of the Act there are a number of provisions relating noise as a statutory nuisance. The consequences of a noise abatement notice invoked using this act are more severe than those under COPA.

Common Law

An individual can seek an injunction under common law, as noise is recognised as a nuisance.

Construction Plant and Equipment (Harmonisation of Noise Emission Standards) Regulations 1985 and 1998

A European Community (EC) re-examination certificate is required before any item of construction plant and equipment may be marketed in the UK. Construction plant and equipment must carry an EC mark to indicate that it conforms to the levels given in the Regulations for that type of machinery. Failure to comply with or contravention of the regulations may result in a fine of up to £2000.

BS 5228 – Noise control on construction and open sites

As the nature of construction work varies so enormously, regulation to control noise requires some flexibility. This standard, comprising of four parts, attempts to provide this. Part 1 gives basic information and procedures; Part 2 deals with construction and demolition, including road maintenance; Part 3 applies to coal extraction by open cast methods; and Part 4 deals with piling operations. The definition of acceptable noise levels is outside the scope of BS 5228.

BS 6472 – Evaluation of human exposure to vibration in buildings

This identifies that a vibration level below 0.1-0.2 mm/s would be imperceptible to most people in most situations, and as such is recommended as a target level to prevent annoyance/disturbance. Higher levels may be allowed, but these would have to be agreed with the local authority environmental health officer, and would need to be below the threshold that would cause damage to structures.

Key guidance – noise

- BS 5228 (1997) Noise control on construction and open sites.

- *How much noise do you make? A guide to assessing and managing noise on construction sites*, CIRIA, PR70, 1999.

- *Ground-borne vibrations arising from piling*, CIRIA, TN142, 1992.

- *Planning to reduce noise exposure in construction*, CIRIA, TN138, 1990.

- *A guide to reducing the exposure of construction workers to noise*, CIRIA, PR120, 1990.

- *Simple noise screens for site use*, CIRIA, SP38, 1985.

- *Noise and vibration from piling operations*, CIRIA, PG9, 1980.

- *Noise Control: Principles and Practice* – Bruel and Kjaer, 1982.

3.3 Dust, Emissions and odours

3.3.1 The importance of controlling dust, emissions and odours

Dust, emissions and odours arising from a site will cause nuisance to neighbours and, at very high concentrations, cause health problems. There is also the potential for legal action, which would have cost and programme implications. Dust, emissions and odours can be particularly hazardous to site staff in confined spaces, so seek information on controls from your company's health and safety officers.

> Dust is generally considered to be any airborne solid matter up to about 2 mm in size. Particle sizes can vary considerably, depending on their origin, and the smallest particles can be inhaled into the lungs. Some dust, such as limestone dust, is chemically active.

3.3.2 Likely impacts, fines and costs

Nuisance to neighbours

Dust emissions and odours can cause nuisance to site neighbours. Nuisance is caused when residents have to re-clean washing, windows, cars, etc. When dredged materials have been placed at the coast to recharge beaches or for reclamation purposes, the dried fine sand can be blown into areas occupied by users. Windblown dust can be unsightly over long distances in scenic areas. In exceptional circumstances, dust can affect health by, for example, causing eye irritation. Asthma can be exacerbated by exposure to respirable dust.

> A company was fined £8500 under air pollution legislation for twice carrying dusty material in uncovered containers for a short distance on a public road.

Dust damage to crops

Claims from farmers are particularly common on rural road projects. Even very low concentrations of dust can affect plant and fruit growth. Plant growth is especially susceptible to dusts that are highly alkaline, for example limestone, and cement dusts. The extent an of effect will be weather-dependant. For example, dust deposited during light rain can cause a crust to form on surfaces. Claims for damages to crops in excess of half a mile from sites have been made, because dust can be blown for long distances.

Impacts on ecology

Dust blowing onto water bodies, such as saline lagoons and saltmarsh, can damage the ecology, particularly if the water body is a sensitive area. With low current speeds and no wave action, dust can increase the turbidity of the water column and potentially smother seabed ecology. In coastal areas, the dust could settle out on vegetation, affecting plant growth, with knock on effects for the species that feed on the vegetation. New growth, in particular that planted as part of the contract (ie revegetating or landscaping the site), may be especially affected.

Impacts on programme and budget

Some contracts may require contractors not to work during times of high wind speeds in a specified direction. Working to comply with strict dust levels can impose cost and/or programme constraints. If a statutory nuisance is caused an abatement notice may be served.

Impacts on plant and equipment

Within the site, dust can cause mechanical or electrical faults to equipment such as computers and electronic control systems. It can increase the abrasion of moving parts and clog filters.

3.3.3 Avoiding dust, emissions and odour problems

To avoid causing complaints, the site should operate a management system that ensures that:

● dust, emissions and odour from general operations are minimised through the adoption of good working practice

● special consideration is given to control measures in circumstances where general good practice may not be sufficient to avoid causing problems.

It is also valuable to keep a record of daily dust conditions (including "background" conditions) in case disputes arise.

If nuisance is still caused following implementation of dust-control measures, find out the reason and offer to put it right by, for example, cleaning windows or washing affected cars.

Dust suppression

As it is difficult to suppress dust once it becomes airborne, it is essential to develop a strategy to stop it being generated. Careful design of construction operations, including the location of stockpiles and batching plant, can reduce dust. Refer to the checklist on the following page.

Damp down using water

The most effective application of water in suppressing dust is by using a fine spray, but its efficiency depends on the speed of the bowser. Repeat spray at regular and frequent intervals, especially during warm and sunny weather when water will evaporate quickly.

Consider spraying:

- unpaved work areas subject to traffic or wind
- structures and buildings during demolition
- sand, spoil and aggregate stockpiles (has only a very temporary and slight effect)
- during loading and unloading of dust-generating materials.

If water is to be abstracted from a watercourse, ensure that permission has been obtained (see Section 3.5.4).

Bowsers can be used to keep exposed earth damp and prevent dust generation

Checklist – avoiding dust generation

Haul Road

- select suitable haul routes away from sensitive sites, if possible
- pave heavily used areas, or use geotextiles (eg around batching plant or haul routes) and sweep these regularly
- provide a length of paved road before the exit from the site
- reduce the width of temporary on-site haul roads (while still allowing two-way traffic) to minimise the surface area from which dust may be produced
- regularly sweep paved access roads and public roads (whilst still allowing two-way traffic) using a vacuum sweeper
- limit vehicle speeds, the slower the vehicles the less dust that will be generated
- damp down, where appropriate.

Demolition

- use enclosed chutes for dropping to ground level demolition materials that have the potential to cause dust
- regularly dampen the chutes
- locate crushing plant for materials away from sensitive sites – consider siting within buildings (use of such plant is controlled – see Key Guidance).

Plant

- clean the wheels of vehicles leaving the site so that mud is not spread on surrounding roads – mud turns to dust when dry
- ensure that exhausts do not discharge directly towards the ground.

Earthworks and excavations

- revegetate or seal temporary or completed earthworks as soon as possible
- keep earthworks damp – try to programme to avoid exceptionally dry weather.

Materials handling and storage

- locate stockpiles out of the wind (or provide wind breaks) to minimise the potential for dust generation
- keep the stockpiles to the minimum practicable height and use gentle slopes
- compact and bind stockpile surfaces (in extreme cases). Revegetate long-term stockpiles
- minimise the storage time for materials on-site
- store materials away from the site boundary and downwind of sensitive areas
- ensure that all dust-generating materials transported to and from site are covered by tarpaulin
- minimise the height of fall of materials
- avoid spillage and clean up any spillage as soon as possible
- damp down, where appropriate.

Damp down using water with chemical additives or binders

Although spraying with water is effective when it is first applied, the effect may not last long. Repeated application, particularly in drought seasons, may itself be environmentally unacceptable. As such, for some applications and particularly for haul roads, the addition of a water-retaining binder may be beneficial. Spraying with water and chemical additives is more effective than using water alone because it reduces the number of passes per day and the volume of water needed.

Several proprietary methods are available:

- calcium chloride – spread on unmade aggregate roads neat at 2kg/m³, or made surface at 1.5 liquor/water dilutions

- magnesium chloride – claimed to be 95% effective on sand and gravel roads

- proprietary brands – polymer or other bonding agents applied as a water additive.

These have been used successfully in the past, especially at mineral workings.

There is no general guidance as to which additive is best. The cost of the additives has to be weighed against savings in water supply, bowser usage and downtime. However, care must be taken to avoid over-application, which may cause pollution.

Care should be taken when spraying. Try to avoid using too much water and creating run-off into nearby watercourses or the sea. It is essential to seek advice from the relevant environment agency before using additives.

Effective planning and management of dust control requires a knowledge of wind conditions for the site. Although prevailing winds across most of the country are from the south-west, this may vary for coastal and marine locations, as well as seasonally. Historical wind data for the site locality can provide guidance on the likely wind speed and direction. This can be obtained from the Meteorological Office in the form of a wind rose (see Section 2.2.2).

If dust is likely to be an important issue, it may be necessary to plan future works against a short-term weather forecast. This can be obtained from the local Meteorological Office. Such information must be used with care, because wind directions and speeds on some sites are significantly influenced by local weather due to adjacent landforms and building features. Local people may be able to provide guidance on local weather patterns.

Dust screening

If dust-generating activities cannot be avoided, it may help to erect screens to act as windbreaks. These can take the form of permeable or semi-permeable fences. However, they can be expensive if they have to be designed to resist high wind speeds. Trees or shrubs planted early as part of site landscaping can provide some screening, likewise retention of existing vegetation (or buildings to be demolished), will aid screening.

Case study

On one site, screening in the form of transparent sheeting was provided alongside bridges over sensitive watercourses.

Dust fence and kerbs on temporary bridge to prevent contamination entering watercourse

Emissions and odours

Processes involving the use of fuels and the heating and drying of materials commonly emit fumes, odours or smoke. It is important to prevent emissions and odours, as far as practicable, both to protect workers and because they may cause nuisance to the public or affect the environment. Where possible, adopt the preventative measures listed in the checklist on the following page. Any works that involve the risk of creating odours (eg works on sewers), should be carefully phased.

3.3 Dust, emissions and odour

> ### Checklist – preventing emissions and odours
>
> **Vehicles and plant**
>
> - keep site vehicles and plant well maintained and regularly serviced
> - ensure that all vehicles comply with MOT emissions standards at all times
> - control deliveries to site and staff car parking, to minimise queuing
> - make sure that engines are switched off when they are not in use (this is particularly important in summer near buildings that have their windows open)
> - keep refuelling areas away from the public.
>
> **No fires on-site**
>
> - do not burn waste materials/tyres on-site.
>
> **Waste storage**
>
> - use covered containers for organic waste and empty frequently
> - remove organic waste (eg weeds and other vegetation), before it begins to decompose.
>
> **Chemicals on-site**
>
> - store fuels and chemicals and other dangerous substances in the appropriate manner (see Section 2.3.4)
> - take account of the wind conditions when arranging activities that are likely to emit aerosols, fumes, odours and smoke
> - position site toilets away from public areas.

3.3.4 Recognising and monitoring problems

Dust Limits

There are no nationally accepted criteria defining levels of dust that cause nuisance or potential health risks. However, there are general guidelines that relate to either the level of deposition of dust (measured as milligrams per square metre per day or in terms of the percentage coverage of a surface area per day) or the level of dust in suspension in the air (measured as micrograms per cubic metre). Levels of acceptability can also relate to the percentage increase in the background deposition rate, which itself can vary substantially.

Dust monitoring and prediction

Whether or not quantitative dust monitoring is imposed on a project, it is recommended that contractors should keep a daily log in the event that a complaint is made subsequently. This should include weather conditions, construction activities, their location on site and visible dust generating activities. A photographic record may also be useful, especially if dust control measures are employed.

If monitoring is imposed, two main methods can be used on-site:

1. Exposing microscope slides or sticky pads for a given period and calculating the deposition rate of dust over the exposed period.
2. Using high-volume samplers to draw air through a filter to measure the volume of dust in the air at the time.

Neither method provides definitive evidence of the impacts of dust and both may be expensive. Experience has shown that much of the dust collected on slides or pads may not have arisen from the construction site. Nevertheless, it may be useful for a contractor to volunteer to monitor dust as a demonstration of commitment to good practice.

For a dust-monitoring programme to give more definitive evidence of construction impacts, it should include both upwind and downwind monitoring of the site and cover a baseline period before construction starts. (The baseline period should ideally cover the same seasons as the construction period.) This level of monitoring will not normally be required by the contract unless the impact of dust is expected to be significant.

3.3.5 Main legislation and key references

Environmental Protection Act 1990 – Statutory nuisance provision

Dust, emissions and odours often generate complaints of discomfort or inconvenience. This may constitute a nuisance under statutory law where the wellbeing and personal comfort of residents and the use and enjoyment of their property is being affected. The problem does not need to cause harm to health, but it must cause inconvenience that is significant enough to be considered a nuisance.

In England and Wales, the person responsible (ie the contractor), can be required by the local authority, through the serving of an abatement notice, to put a stop to a statutory nuisance. (In Scotland the responsibility lies with SEPA). Aggrieved individuals can also apply to the magistrates for an abatement order to stop the nuisance. Breach of an abatement notice or order is a criminal offence.

Clean Air Act 1993

In England, Wales and Scotland, this is the primary legislative means of control over smoke, grit and dust. It is generally enforced by local authorities, and applies to emissions of dark smoke from industrial or trade premises that originate from sources other than chimneys.

3.3 Dust, emissions and odour

Demolition and construction have been found to be "trade processes" for the purposes of this legislation, and a bonfire on a demolition site emitting dark smoke has also been found to be within the scope of the Act. However, there are also regulations that exempt emissions from the burning of timber and most other waste resulting from demolition of a building or of a site, as well as emissions from tar, pitch, asphalt or other matter used in connection with surfacing.

Key guidance – Dust, emissions and odours

- Mobile Crushing and Screening Processes, 1996, Department of the Environment PG3/16 (96).

- Minerals Planning Guidance: The control of noise at surface mineral workings MPG 11, Consultation Paper, Office of the Deputy Prime Minister, 2000.

- Environment Agency, SEPA and Environment and Heritage Service Pollution Prevention Guidance:
  - PPG 5 Works in, near or liable to affect watercourses
  - PPG 6 Working at construction and demolition sites
  - PPG 23 Maintenance of structures over water.

Ground and sediment contamination

3.4 Ground and sediment contamination

If contamination is likely to be encountered on site, the construction contract should define the methods for dealing with it. The contract will usually refer to the guidance issued by statutory authorities on how to cope with the contamination. This type of detailed advice is beyond the scope of this guide – look for further advice in the "key guidance" provided below.

This section does, however, provide general advice on how to deal with contamination (both expected and unexpected), and how to avoid causing and spreading contamination.

3.4.1 Avoiding or containing land or sediment contamination

Encountering ground contamination may result in the following problems

- health and safety impacts on staff and the surrounding community through exposure to contaminants

- liability for the cost of disposal or remediation of contamination (depending on the contract conditions)

- liability for costs arising from unexpected spreading or making existing contamination worse

- delays to the programme and additional costs associated in dealing with unexpected or accidental contamination

- pollution of groundwater or surrounding watercourses

- pollution of surrounding land

- harm to local wildlife and habitats through exposure to contaminants.

Sediment contamination may result in many of the above problems and additionally may be of particular concern due to the risk of water-borne contaminants being released outside of the site. Contaminants contained in estuarine sediments, for example, may be re-suspended and partially dispersed over a wide area as a result of works below mean high water (eg piling or dredging). Extended exposure to humans and wildlife may also cause worry through bioaccumulation and magnification within the marine food chain.

When managing contaminated sediments it is essential that it is not allowed to spread and that it is recovered and disposed of appropriately. When dredging, this may involve not working an area of contamination and/or ensuring that the material is disposed of in a manner agreed upon with the correct licensing authority (see Section 3.1.6).

3.4 Ground and sediment contamination

3.4.2 Legal implications of contamination

A contractor will be legally and financially liable for clean up if he has **"caused or knowingly permitted"** contamination to occur. This liability may include fines and extends to the contamination of all "controlled waters", including that from existing contaminated land. Therefore, even if the contractor was not responsible for causing the existing contamination, but has knowingly permitted it to contaminate controlled waters by his actions, he will be liable. This may often be the case in heavily industrialised estuarine areas which have been historically contaminated.

Most costs are likely to result from any obligation that the contractor has to decontaminate the land. This is an enforceable action that can be used by the local authority, the costs of which could be considerable. It is therefore essential that a contractor ensures that he is satisfied with the level of risk of contamination being present on-site before construction starts.

3.4.3 Main causes of problems and incidents

Generally, contamination results from previous uses of the site (or adjacent land), for example, industrial use, waste disposal and ship yards. Contaminated sediments are likely to be present at sewerage or other outfalls, or where previous pollution incidents have occurred. Be aware that incidents during construction can also lead to ground and sediment contamination, as shown below:

Examples of how problems with contamination may arise

Existing contamination:

- encountering contamination during the works
- handling or excavating contaminated ground
- handling or dredging contaminated sediment.

Ground sediment and contamination

Causing or spreading contamination:

- windblown contaminated dust arising from excavation, loading of lorries and transportation
- wind blown smells from wet material as it dries
- stockpiling contaminated material on clean ground in the course of the works site
- stockpiling materials containing contaminants liable to leach out to underlying ground or nearby water bodies, such as saline lagoons
- slippage or discarding of contaminated land into water
- spillage of contaminants such as oil onto the ground or into water during construction
- de-watering that draws in contaminated groundwater from adjacent sites
- discharge of contaminated de-watering output into nearby water bodies
- disposal, resuspension and spillage of contaminated sediment from dredging operations.

Disturbing unexpected archaeological finds, such as burial grounds, may also pose a health risk to the workforce.

Checklist – avoiding causing or spreading contamination

- Do not stockpile contaminated soil unless it cannot be avoided. If this is necessary, stockpile only on a hardstanding area away from the sea or watercourses. Drainage run-off must be contained and disposed of appropriately to avoid discharge to water bodies. The stockpile may also need to be covered to prevent windblown dust or to minimise the ingress of rainwater or sea spray.

- Be especially vigilant when working close to or within tidal limits about the presence of contaminated material, spillage of materials from plant and possible instability.

- Do not pile or dredge into contaminated sediments without containment measures being in place or prior targeted removal of the contaminated material.

- Prevent the spread of contaminated dust (ie keep damp – Section 3.3.3).

- Be careful when handling, storing and using oils and chemicals (Section 2.3.4).

3.4.4 Avoiding these problems

Initially, the responsibility lies with the client for carrying out a site soil or sediment survey and deducing the risks from any contamination that may be present. However, the contractor is advised to check whether this has been done satisfactorily. A preliminary investigation should have included an investigation of the site history and its surroundings, involving examination of published maps, plans and photographs and existing site records. Information relevant to preliminary investigations includes:

- the history of the site (details of its owners, occupiers and users)
- the processes used (including their locations, raw materials, products, waste residues and methods of disposal)
- the layout of the site above and below ground at each stage of development (including roadways, storage areas and other hard cover areas)
- the presence of waste disposal tips, made ground, abandoned pits and quarries, with or without standing water
- mining history (including shafts and roadways)
- information on geology, hydrology (including the presence of groundwater and surface water) and the tidal conditions
- any potential contamination of sites, past or present, in the area adjacent to the site.

If the preliminary investigation finds that contamination is probable, an exploratory investigation is normally undertaken to define the type, concentration and extent of any contamination on the site. If the site manager suspects that contamination might be an issue and is concerned that there is a lack of information, expert advice should be sought from the relevant environment agency.

Exploratory contamination survey at a coastal site in Falmouth

Ground and sediment contamination

Information from phase 1 (preliminary) and phase 2 (exploratory) investigations should have been supplied to the contractor as part of the health and safety plan. The contractor will be required to prepare health and safety risk assessments and detailed method statements, which will state the approach to be taken in dealing with any contamination on the site.

The contractor should also be extremely aware of the risk of discovering unexploded ordnance on the foreshore or at sea. If ordnance is found on your site, you should immediately contact the emergency services.

It is always possible that contamination will not have been located during the investigations but will be uncovered during the site works. This is most likely to occur at sites with an industrial history, although old waste tips may be found on any site. Therefore, site staff – especially excavator operators – should be vigilant during excavations.

3.4.5 Recognising problems and taking actions

Some incidences of contamination, such as when a large spill of a pollutant occurs, will be easy to spot, for others it will be necessary to look for a range of tell-tale signs during boring, digging, excavating, dredging and similar operations.

> If suspected contamination is discovered, do the following:
>
> - stop work immediately
> - seal off the area
> - report the discovery to the site manager
> - the site manager should seek expert advice from the relevant environment agency or company environmental representative.

3.4 Ground sediment and contamination

Checklist – spotting incidents of contamination

- discoloured soil (eg chemical residues)
- fibrous texture to the soil (eg asbestos)
- presence of foreign objects (eg chemical/oil containers)
- evidence of previous soil workings
- evidence of underground structure and tanks
- existence of waste pits
- made ground (ie artificial ground where ground level is raised by man's activities and not due to a natural cause)
- old drain runs and contamination within buildings, tanks, flues etc
- release of fumes and smells (such as petrol, oils, bad eggs etc)
- sediment close to outfalls or previous pollution incidents
- sediments that leave an oily sheen or iridescence when in contact with water
- oily sheen on water surfaces may indicate leaching of contaminants from adjacent soils
- material behind retaining walls and dock walls where contaminated backfill may have been used or liquid contaminants may have been trapped.

It is good practice for the contractor to have in place a contingency plan for the unforeseen discovery of contamination or a potential pollution incident that could lead to contamination.

> If ASBESTOS is uncovered re-cover it temporarily to prevent its release to the atmosphere and seek expert advice.

3.4.6 Main legislation and key references

Legislation

There is no legislation that sets out specifically to address contaminated land and sediment issues, though several statutes exist which influence how contaminated land issues are managed, including:

- The Environmental Protection Act (prescribed processes and substances) 1990 – stipulates substances where release into the environment is controlled (in Great Britain).

Ground sediment and contamination 3.4

- The Environmental Protection Act 1990 (as amended by The Environment Act 1995), identifies contaminated land as:

  - land that is (or has the potential to) causing significant harm

  - land that is polluting (or has the potential to pollute) controlled waters.

- Contaminated Land (England) Regulations 2000 & Part III of the Waste and Contaminated Land (Northern Ireland) Order 1997 – Under this legislation, local authorities have the power to raise a remediation notice to specify what action needs to be taken by the person who contaminated the land. Failure to comply with a remediation notice is an offence. Similar regulations were brought into force in Scotland in 2000 (guidance is provided in Planning Advice Note (PAN) 30);

- Water Resources Act 1991 – This act empowers the Environment Agency in England and Wales to serve a "works notice" on any person who has caused or knowingly permitted a pollutant to enter a controlled water, including from contaminated land, requiring them to deal with the problem; and

- The Control of Pollution (Oil Storage) (England) Regulations 2001 detail exact requirements for bunding stored oil and lubricants in quantities more than 200 litres.

Key guidance – ground and sediment contamination

- BSI DRAFT for Development DD175:1998 Code of Practice for the identification of Potentially Contaminated Land and its Investigation
- *Environmental good practice on site*, CIRIA C502, 1999
- *A guide to safe working on contaminated sites*, CIRIA R132, 1996
- HSG66 Protection of Workers and the General Public during Development of Contaminated Land, HSE
- Environment Agency, SEPA and Environment and Heritage Service, Pollution Prevention Guidelines (PPG):
  - PPG1   General guide to prevention of pollution of controlled waters
  - PPG2   Above ground oil storage tanks
  - PPG5   Works in, near or liable to affect watercourses
  - PPG6   Working at demolition and construction sites
  - PPG8   Safe storage and disposal of used oils;
  - PPG13   The use of high pressure and steam cleaners
  - PPG20   Dewatering underground ducts and chambers
  - PPG21   Pollution Incident Response Planning
  - PPG23   Maintenance of structures over water.
- Other relevant environment agency publications:
  - Silt pollution and how to avoid it
  - Spillage pollution and how to avoid it
  - Follow the oil care code
  - Oil care at work.

3.5 Water quality

3.5 Water Quality

3.5.1 Protecting Water Quality

Once a pollutant enters the sea or a watercourse it is extremely difficult to remove or control. Consequently, it is vital that appropriate steps are taken to prevent water pollution when working on-site. Water quality is a key factor in determining the health of the marine environment and fisheries, and can also impact on a range of additional factors, such as tourism and recreation in coastal areas. Importantly it must be remembered that coastal waters are "controlled waters" and it is an offence to pollute them, deliberately or accidentally.

There are many materials and wastes or by-products that arise from construction activities and which may affect coastal and marine water bodies, including:

- fine materials (ie silts and clays)
- cement
- oil and chemicals (ie from plant machinery and processes)
- other wastes such as woods, plastics, sewerage and building rubble.

Additionally, water bodies may be affected by cleaning and repainting processes, and by the re-suspension of previously deposited contaminants.

 Always read the labels and forms provided with your material and supply consignments. Check directions for special handling and care, and always follow the instructions.

3.5.2 Likely impacts, fines and costs

Through affecting water quality, pollutants can greatly impact on fisheries and other important wildlife. There are also potential effects on local tourism and leisure resources should bathing water quality be affected.

Blue Flag beaches

The award of a "Blue Flag" means that a beach area has complied with 27 criteria relating to water quality, environmental education, management and safety. As of 2002, there are 83 Blue Flag beaches in the UK, all of which warrant specific care and attention during any works. Information is available from www.blueflag.org/

Potential impacts on the environment due to water quality problems are numerous. High levels of silt and clay can damage fish gills and eventually kill them. It can also smother shellfish stocks, other invertebrates and sensitive plant life, which are themselves a food source for fish. Silt deposited on the seabed may prevent fish spawning and suffocate eggs. Concrete and cement can change the chemical balance of the water environment (both are highly alkaline). As such, please note that pollutants can temporarily or permanently damage the ecological balance of the seabed and/or shoreline.

Oil pollution in coastal and marine environments can cause substantial water quality problems, even in low quantities, because oil spreads rapidly on the surface. It directly affects fish and other aquatic life and causes distinctive contamination problems for coastlines. Other important animals or sea birds can also be seriously affected by oil. Oil is both expensive and difficult to deal with.

> The owners of a container ship caught red-handed discharging oil off Land's End were fined £250 000 in a prosecution brought by the Maritime and Coastguard Agency in Sept 1998.

In addition to cleanup costs, fines and legal fees, the overall costs of a water pollution incident will include disruption to construction activities, non-productive time for the equipment and personnel, and the potential loss of weather windows.

3.5.3 The main risks

Many construction activities pose a risk to water quality. Problems can potentially occur from any of the following:

- water abstraction
- water disposal
- spillage
- resuspension of sediments
- effluent from washing/cleaning operations
- solid wastes
- surface water run off.

3.5 Water quality

3.5.4 Maintaining water quality

General good practice

Before commencing construction it is essential to undertake the following checks:

Checklist – water quality

- Examine the contract for conditions relating to water quality.

- Consider undertaking review of existing survey data to establish the quality of the water. This data may be useful if an incident occurs.

- Establish and mark the location of any surface water drains and foul sewers on-site.

- Before commencing, look out for underground pipes and tanks; although these could be de-commissioned, they may still contain enough product residues of the original contents to cause a potential pollutant incident. They may also act as conduit for pollution spills on-site.

- Carry out regular inspections of all discharges, drainage systems, interceptors and watercourses to check that these are in good working order.

Managing the risks to water

A structured approach is recommended for managing water on-site successfully to avoid causing pollution and to minimise costs and effort. The required steps are summarised below.

Checklist – managing the risks to water

STEP 1 *Evaluate the potential challenges and risks for the project*

Water pollution may arise from both activity and inactivity on-site. Identify the potential sources of pollution and evaluate the risk of accidents/spills etc. Risks for the project might include: spillage due to incorrect handling and storage procedures; washout from concreting operations; and works in contaminated sediment.

STEP 2 *Identify appropriate control and management methods for each potential issue identified in Step 1*

Identify the measures and techniques that will need to be utilised to minimise and avoid construction risk. Some of the approaches that can be adopted are outlined in Section 3.1.5.

STEP 3 *Ensure compliance and monitor implementation*

Water pollution incidents usually arise as a result of ignorance, negligence or vandalism, so guard against each of these:

- Predict potential pollution incidents by undertaking a risk assessment.

- Provide training to eliminate ignorance (include subcontractors).

- Combat negligence by supervising site personnel; and

- Secure sites against vandalism.

STEP 4 *Adopt an Emergency Response Plan*

Even with the best controls in place, pollution incidents may occur. Therefore, ensure that the site has an Emergency Response Plan, suitable equipment and that all relevant staff know how to put it into practice.

Dedicated concrete washing-out area

Abstracting water

In many cases it may be necessary to obtain a licence to abstract water for use on site. If abstraction is to take place, check to see whether this consent is in place and, if not, whether it is required. For further information, contact your company's environmental representative or the relevant environment agency.

3.5 Water quality

Disposing of water from a site

This applies to a wide range of discharge types, both polluted and unpolluted. Construction site runoff and all waste waters arising (including domestic sewage), must be disposed of in accordance with the requirements of the relevant regulatory authorities, for example:

● Consent is required from the local sewerage undertaker to discharge effluent to public sewers.

● Consent is required from the relevant environment agency to discharge direct to controlled waters. The consent will set limits for allowable concentrations of pollutants and flow rates. It may also prescribe peak flow rates for unpolluted discharges.

Before discharging any water, ensure that permission has been obtained to do so and that the discharge will comply with any conditions specified in that permission. This may require discharges to be monitored and liaison to be carried out with the relevant regulatory authorities.

> Obtaining consents may take time, they may also require detailed information of the type and nature of water to be discharged, so it is essential to plan ahead.

If a consent to discharge is not obtained, wastewater will have to be stored and pumped into a tanker for off-site disposal, which may be costly. If small quantities of waste water are generated, pump it into clearly labelled tanks for removal off site at a later date.

Discharging silty water

To establish the best approach for your site, review the following prioritised options; those at the top of the list are the least expensive and cause least risk of accidental pollution:

1. Pump to grassland or other excavation/soakaway – these areas should preferably be well away from main site excavations to avoid re-circulation though the ground. The silty water should contain no chemical pollutants or biological pollutants. Before pumping to grassland check its conservation importance (contact your relevant conservation agency).

2. Pump to sewer (obtain licence from the sewerage undertaker).

3. Pump to an adequately sized settlement tank.

4. Pass through filtration system.

5. Use flocculents in conjunction with a settling tank (subject to approval by the appropriate environment agency).

6. Pump into a tanker and dispose off site.

> The most common form of water pollution from construction is suspended sediments – more commonly known as silty water, muddy water or dirty water.

The preferred option will depend on a number of factors, including:

- agreement of the appropriate environment agency
- the quantities of water involved
- whether areas are available for storage and treatment
- the level of any charges to be levied by the sewerage authority
- the degree of contamination of the water
- the characteristics of the sediment.

Avoiding spillage

There are many precautions that can be taken to avoid spillage. These are detailed in the text and checklist that follow, and include the use of bunds around oil storage tanks and the use of drip trays for mobile plant. See C502 for further detail.

> A contractor was fined £7500 and ordered to pay costs of £5438 on 13 March 2000 after pleading guilty to polluting Portsmouth harbour with oil, contrary to Section 85 of the Water Resources Act 1991.

Managing re-suspension of sediments

During dredging, sediment is brought back into suspension. Finer sediments and any pollutants which may be entrained with them are likely to be retained in or re-enter the water column within the area being dredged and then be moved elsewhere. The pollutants could include heavy metals (in particular tributyltin (TBT) in the vicinity of ship repair activities), and pathogenic organisms (bacteria, viruses, etc), which could adversely affect nearby bathing waters.

Managing liquid wastes

Cleaning and repainting processes over, or adjacent to, water has the potential to pollute. Where possible, physical cleaning methods (eg wire brushing, sand or grit blasting), should be adopted in preference to liquid chemicals, such as caustic and acid solution. If such liquids are to be used then the effluent must be fully contained (ie by the use of a bund or tray).

3.5 Water quality

Temporary storage
bund for oil and
chemical storage

Checklist – storing and using fuel and oil

- Consider whether fuel storage is needed on-site, how much is to be stored and how – in large tanks, small stores or a mobile bowser.

- Check whether your sub-contractors have adequate fuel storage facilities.

- Fuel and oil stores must be located away from the site drainage system and the shoreline. If this is not possible, ensure adequate measures are identified to prevent or contain any spillage (eg blocking drainage points).

- Fuel and oil stores should be kept away from vehicle access routes to prevent collisions.

- Fuel and oil storage must be sited on an impermeable base within a bund to contain at least 110 per cent of the maximum capacity. All ancillary equipment (valves, hoses etc), should be contained securely within the bund when not in use.

- Ensure that tanks are correctly labelled as to their contents and capacities.

- Keep a store of spill response equipment at the fuel facility and bowsers.

- Guard the facility against vandalism and theft, the facility should be locked off when not in use.

- Use drip trays under all static plant (eg pumps and generators), particularly during refuelling from mobile plant, and empty them regularly.

Water quality 3.5

Managing solid wastes

When working on structures over, or adjacent to, water the environment agencies recommend that all solid wastes are prevented from falling into the sea or onto any embankment, quay etc. Provision for the collection of solid debris, including wastes, should be incorporated into working methods. Any wastes falling into the water should be removed immediately.

Managing surface water runoff

Surface water running across or ponding on a site may cause water management or pollution problems. For example, more than 25 tonnes of sediment can be eroded per hectare of site in a year. The solution is to control surface water so that it does not run into excavations, disturbed ground or onto haul roads. Ensure that the water collection system is adequate to allow for the controlled release of storm flows. Protect water bodies from silty run off from disturbed ground (on haul roads or from top soil stripping), and soil stock piles.

In dry weather, large quantities of mud and oils can build up on areas of hardstanding. If these are not cleared frequently, a sudden shower can wash them into the sea or a watercourse, giving very high pollutant loads. Therefore, hardstanding and road surfaces must be kept clean.

Useful guidance – concrete, cement and bentonite

- Concrete, cement and bentonite are highly alkaline and corrosive and can have a devastating impact upon water quality.

- Take particular care (ie ensure operations are planned and supervised), when producing, transporting and placing these materials, especially if working next to the shoreline or a watercourse.

- Use methods to minimise grout loss during shutter pours.

- Place covers over freshly poured concrete to prevent the surface washing away in heavy rain.

- Do not hose down spills of concrete, cement or bentonite into surface water drains.

- Washout should be carried out in a designated impermeable and contained area and washout water should not be allowed to flow or drain into the sea or any drains.

- Try to reuse washout water as much as possible, then dispose of it by tankering of site in accordance with "duty of care" or discharging to foul sewer with agreement from the sewerage undertaker.

- Washout water and water from excavations may require adjustment of pH in a lagoon prior to discharge (ie too alkaline). Obtain specialist advice from the relevant environment agency as acid conditions can also have a serious effect on water quality.

3.5.5 Recognising issues and taking action

The chemical analysis of water samples for trace quantities of contaminants or for particular pollutants can be a specialised task. However, much can be learned from the visual appearance of a water sample and this may be supplemented by the use of simple on-site test kits to gain an appreciation of the polluting potential of the sample. The colour, odour, level of suspended solids and presence of an oil film may provide an insight into the potential problems associated with a water sample.

The use of pH papers and tests strips, which show a colour change to differing acidic or alkaline conditions, can also indicate the presence of specific contaminants on-site. For instance, high pH rinse waters from concrete batching plants or grouting work can be toxic to aquatic systems and may cause a severe incident.

If a potential problem is recognised, action must be taken immediately to minimise the potential damage. Advanced planning will be required to put in place an Emergency Response Plan to deal with such occurrences.

An effective emergency response system relies on the following:

- an Emergency Response Plan
- suitable emergency equipment and associated staff training
- definition of responsibilities
- contact numbers
- training in implementation (see Section 2.1.5).

Emergency response

In a pollution incident or suspected pollution incident, the Emergency Response Plan for the site must be followed. In the event of the silting, erosion or pollution of coastal waters, the site manager should call the emergency pollution line of the relevant environment agency immediately (in the UK this is 0800 807060). If the incident affects the sea below the High Water Mark, the local office of the Maritime and Coastguard Agency should also be contacted. Following clean-up, the incident must be reported to your company's environmental representative so that lessons can be learned for the future.

Site managers should ensure that necessary information and equipment is at hand, that it is renewed and maintained regularly and that staff know where it is stored and how it should be used. In some instances, for example if a construction project is particularly large or the environmental risk considerable, it may be worth setting up a spillage control contract with a specialist pollution control contractor.

Emergency Response Plan

All appropriate staff must be fully aware of the site's Emergency Response Plan and know where to find it and how to use it. It is also essential that staff appreciate the health and safety risks that may be present in executing an Emergency Response Plan on the coast or at sea.

The Emergency Response Plan should be drawn up in consultation with the Emergency Services, the Local Authority, the relevant environment agency, and the Maritime and Coastguard Agency. Some local authorities and harbour areas will have existing Emergency Response Plans.

Key guidance

● Environment Agency, SEPA and Environment and Heritage Service

   – PPG 21 Pollution Incident Response Planning.

Example of a typical Emergency Response Plan

1. In case of spillage of oils and chemicals, report immediately to the nominated manager/supervisor, who should report the incident to the relevant environment agency (and Coast Guard Agency, if applicable), and/or sewerage undertaker, along with the company's specialist spill control contractors, where relevant. Staff and members of the general public should be moved from the affected areas.

2. Assess the risk of tackling the spill, if safe to do so.

3. Try to identify the source of pollution and stop the flow immediately. Switch off sources of ignition.

4. Try to contain the spill or prevent it spreading:

   On land: – check drainage plans – where will the spillage go?
   – divert from drains/watercourses where possible
   – dam the flow with earth/sand/polythene.

   On water: – install containment booms.

5. On land: – do not wash down the spillage and do not use detergents;
   – use absorbent pads or sand to mop it up
   – make sure that materials used are easily recoverable.

   On water: – install recovery equipment recommended by specialists (eg mop, rotating disc or other skimmer)
   – do not use dispersants
   – make sure that materials used are easily recoverable.

Example of a typical Emergency Response Plan (cont)		
6	On land:	– shovel contaminated sand/earth/granules into "double bags" and dispose according to relevant waste management legislation – any oil pools should be removed by a suction system (eg vacuum unit or sludge-gulper) first.
	On water:	– store the recovered pollutant in appropriate tank(s) for subsequent off-site disposal.

Responsibilities

Ensure that all relevant staff are aware of their own and others regular management and emergency response responsibilities/duties. Contingencies for absence should be established where possible. See Section 2.1.3 for further detail on responsibility of staff on-site.

Ensure that the contact details (working and non-working hours), for the following groups are available:

- site management personnel, including sub-contractors
- the environmental representative for your company
- emergency services and Coastguard
- the relevant environment agencies
- local authority's environmental health department (or officer)
- sewerage undertaker
- equipment suppliers
- liquid waste disposal contractors
- specialist spillage control contractors (where relevant).

Equipment

Emergency spill kits are available for dealing with spillage (including oils and chemicals), both on land and water. These should be obtained from a reputable supplier. The contents of the kit will depend on the project but could include:

- oil-absorbent granule;
- floating booms (either containment or absorbent)
- absorbent mats
- polythene sheeting
- polythene sacks (for double bagging waste)
- ropes, anchors or wooden stakes (for securing booms on water).

Spill kits should be stored in marked bag(s) or container(s) in well sign-posted location(s). They should be stored close to where they are likely to be needed. It is recommended that tamper evident seals be fitted on the containers so that it is apparent when equipment has been used. Regular checks should be made to ensure that all of the equipment is present, undamaged and that spares are available as required.

As part of any Emergency Response Planning, it is essential that the most suitable types of equipment for use in spills are selected. Selection should be based on risk assessments and, if appropriate, advice from specialists. Oil and chemical absorbent kits differ in their properties and cannot be used in combination. Absorbent kit is effective but expensive; containment kit is effective and re-usable, and can be more suitable for dealing with larger spills in conjunction with recovery equipment. It is important to check that booms are of suitable size for the application and type of conditions, and that suitable anchoring arrangements can be made.

Buckets of sand, earth, straw bales and rags are good for cleaning up small spills on land, but care should be taken in a coastal environment as consideration must be given to their recovery. If working in a particularly vulnerable environment (ie saltmarsh, offshore reef), or with large quantities of liquid products, it may be worth approaching a specialist spill control equipment supplier.

Training

Manufacturers of spill kits often provide training in their use and it is recommended that this be implemented. It is important that staff fully appreciate the risks associated with emergency response in coastal and marine environments. If the project is large or in an area of high environmental risk it is recommended that a practice response exercise is carried out early on in the work.

3.5.6 Main legislation and key references

It is important to remember that under current legislation in England and Wales the contractor/site occupier is responsible for all pollution incidents. Even if vandals are the cause of an incident, the contractor/site occupier will still legally be responsible. The following legislation is of key importance:

Water Resources Act 1991 (England and Wales)

It is a criminal offence to cause or knowingly permit any poisonous, noxious or polluting matter or any solid waste matter (which includes silt, concrete, cement, oil, petroleum spirit, sewage or other polluting matter), to enter any controlled waters unless the discharge is authorised. Road drains and surface water gullies generally discharge into controlled waters. The Control of Pollution Act (1974 and amendments) in Scotland has the same provisions (SEPA).

3.5 Water quality

Water Industry Act 1991 (England and Wales)

An occupier of trade premises (which includes a construction site), is committing an offence if trade effluent is discharged into a sewerage system without the sewerage undertaker's consent.

> The maximum penalties on summary conviction for causing or knowingly permitting a pollutant to enter controlled waters (for staff throughout the organisation) are:
>
> - imprisonment for up to six months or a fine not exceeding £20 000, or both, in a magistrates court
> - imprisonment for up to five years or an unlimited fine, or both, in a Crown Court.

Environmental Protection Act 1990

In Great Britain, all waste produced is subject to "duty of care" under this Act and, therefore, contractors have a duty to ensure that all wastes are controlled and disposed of in such a way as not to cause pollution or environmental harm.

Environment Act 1995

The Environment Act 1995 further strengthens the provisions available to the relevant environment agency (in England, Wales and Scotland), to prevent pollution incidents, undertake anti-pollution works or to serve notice on any person in situations where polluting matter has entered, or is likely to enter, any controlled water. A works notice, issued under the Anti-Pollution Works Regulations 1999, can require the person to:

- remove or dispose of the polluting matter – and
- remedy the pollution and restore the affected areas of water.

The Control of Pollution (Oil Storage) (England) Regulations 2001

These Regulations place a range of conditions on the storage of oil in above ground containers (with capacity exceeding 200 litres). Key features of the standard include:

- tanks, drums and containers must be strong enough to hold the oil without bursting
- a bund or drip tray must be provided to catch any oil leaks from the container, or its pipe work and fittings
- the bund must be sufficient to contain 110% of the capacity of the oil container (the Regulations provide additional information for multiple containers).

The penalties for summary conviction on contravening the Control of Pollution Regulations are:

- A fine not exceeding £5000 in a magistrate's court; and
- An unlimited fine in a Crown Court.

Key guidance – water quality

- The following PPG Notes are available free of charge from the Environment Agency (England and Wales), SEPA, and the Environment and Heritage Service of Northern Ireland:
  - PPG1   General Guide to the Prevention of Pollution
  - PPG2   Above Ground Oil Storage Tanks
  - PPG4   Disposal of Sewage Where No Mains Drainage is Available
  - PPG5   Works in, Near, or Liable to Affect Watercourses
  - PPG6   Working at Construction and Demolition Sites
  - PPG8   Safe Storage and Disposal of Used Oils
  - PPG11   Preventing Pollution at Industrial Sites
  - PPG18   Managing Fire Water and Major Spillages
  - PPG21   Pollution Incident Response Planning
  - PPG23   Maintenance of Structures Over Water
  - PPG26   Storage and Handling of Drums and Intermediate Bulk Containers.
- In addition, the following are also available from the relevant environment agency:
  - Oil Storage Regulations
  - Oil Care, Follow the Code
  - River Pollution and how to avoid it
  - Silt Pollution and how to avoid it.

3.6 Wildlife and natural features

In this guide, the terms "Wildlife", "Species" and "Habitats" are taken to mean all living things, such as trees, flowering plants, insects, birds and mammals and the habitats in which they live. "Natural Feature" is used to encompass the physical surroundings, structures, landforms and/or inherent processes (ie geology and geomorphology), usually found on the coast and in marine areas.

3.6.1 Wildlife value and conservation

Wildlife and natural features have become widely recognised as the key component of a healthy environment and are highly valued by the general public. The level of protection given to wildlife and natural features in the coastal zone is increasing through legal controls and in contract conditions. Usually, the developer has responsibility for investigating the ecological interests, sensitivities and constraints of a site and defining them for the contractor. However, many coastal and marine issues will require specialist experience so, in many cases, it will be necessary to consult an environmental expert – for example a nature conservation body such as English Nature. If contractors fail to meet their legal and contractual requirements sanctions may be imposed which can affect the cost and the programme of the project.

Be aware! Unexpected rare wildlife (plant or animal) finds can arise during works. The contractor has the responsibility to deal with these in the correct manner. This may affect your works.

3.6.2 Fines and costs

In coastal and marine waters, many of the species present are protected under international agreement through various forms of legislation. UK marine site legislation is being strengthened and potential fines for damage or disturbance to a protected site or species are increasing significantly.

Until recently, in England and Wales, the fine for damage to a Site of Special Scientific Interest (SSSI) was around £2500. However, under changes to existing legislation (see Section 3.6.8), it is now possible to prosecute in a magistrate's court, where fines will be up to £20 000, and in Crown Court where fines will be unlimited. Offenders may also be ordered to restore the damage caused.

The conservation agencies

This term is used here to represent the following organisations that have a statutory responsibility for promoting the conservation of wildlife and natural features within the UK:

- English Nature
- Countryside Council for Wales
- Northern Ireland Environment and Heritage Service
- Scottish Natural Heritage.

Their remit includes identifying designations and protecting sites of ecological, geological and geomorphological importance and providing advice on species protected under UK and international legislation. Within each region there are additional bodies that have a non-statutory environmental remit. These include County Wildlife Trusts, local authorities and national and local environmental groups such as the Marine Conservation Society, the Royal Society for the Protection of Birds (RSPB) and the World Wildlife Fund for Nature (WWF).

3.6.3 Problems and incidents

There are three main reasons for considering ecological issues when working in the coastal zone or at sea:

Where species or areas have been identified for particular protection

In this instance, studies will have already been carried out to determine the likely implications of construction and acceptable working practices. Site staff should be made aware of any identified special conditions that they should follow to protect particular species or areas of the site. In marine areas, the important species are likely to be birds and marine mammals (ie whales, dolphins, seals etc), but could equally be fish and invertebrates. Important habitats may include saltmarsh, mudflats, vegetated shingle, cliffs, sea caves, reefs and sub-tidal sandbanks.

If you have any questions or uncertainties regarding such issues, contact your company's environmental representative in the first instance. Relevant organisations such as the conservation agencies, the Wildlife Trusts and other organisations with a direct interest in or responsibility for the environment will also be able to provide specialist advice, as appropriate (eg the Shark Trust, Wildfowl and Wetlands Trust).

Conservation agencies have responsibility for nature conservation issues within UK territorial waters (12 nautical miles offshore). The Joint Nature Conservation Committee (JNCC) is responsible for conservation issues, out to the limit of UK waters (ie 200 miles offshore).

Where protected species are discovered when the contractor is already on-site and works have begun

Work should be stopped immediately, and the site manager and environmental representative should seek expert advice on how to proceed. Negotiations with the relevant conservation agencies may have to take place to discuss the best way forward. Such species might include all breeding birds, seals, whales and dolphins, and basking sharks.

To minimise general on-site damage to wildlife and natural features

Construction managers and site personnel should not only make attempts to protect particular species and designated sites but must take a responsible attitude to the natural environment as a whole. This is especially true of the marine environment, as it is an open and dynamic system and it is often difficult to isolate problems to one single area.

Coastal and marine areas have few boundaries that can be "fenced off" and so best practice approaches should be adopted to reduce the potential for temporary or permanent impacts on the surrounding ecology.

Construction activities can affect wildlife through effects such as:

- changes in water quality, pH, salinity, turbidity
- oxygen depletion
- nutrient enrichment
- inputs of foreign materials, substances and species
- interruption to migratory pathways (eg some fish species)
- habitat fragmentation
- disturbance to breeding, migrating and wintering bird species
- disturbance to whales, dolphins, porpoises and basking sharks
- restricting access to habitats used during extreme weather conditions
- high noise and vibration levels
- changes in light regime
- trampling of vegetation or sedentary animal species
- destruction of places inhabited by plants or animals.

Please note that the above factors should be fully considered at the design and planning stages of a development. Conditions to reduce or prevent potential impacts (if applicable), are likely to be attached to the planning consents and construction contract.

National Nature Reserves (NNRs)

NNRs are places where wildlife comes first, where you must be careful not to disturb or damage sensitive and fragile habitats and species. They are established to protect the most important areas of wildlife habitat and geological formations in Great Britain. Every reserve has its own management plan which is updated every five years, usually by the site manager. Examples include Lindisfarne, The Wash and Dungeness.

Marine Nature Reserves (MNRs) may extend from the High Water Mark out to three nautical miles offshore. They are designated with the explicit purpose of conserving marine flora, fauna, geological and physiological features and for providing opportunities for study and research. Examples include the islands of Lundy and Skomer.

Construction of Shaw's Jetty on Lundy Island using drill rig and jack-up rig (*Charlotte Louise*) in 1999.

3.6.4 Wildlife issues

Avoidance of construction related problems in the marine and coastal environment can be achieved through ensuring a good prior knowledge of the ecological interest of the construction site and its surrounding area. Firstly, it is important to ensure that all designated ecological sites and/or protected species have been identified and that this information has been passed on to all site staff and your sub-contractors.

> **Off-site assembly**
>
> In sensitive areas, off-site assembly is often recommended to minimise or avoid the impact of works on local fauna and flora. Pre-assembled elements are delivered as required thus limiting noise, vibration, dust and other disrupting influences. However, contractors have a responsibility to ensure that the off-site assembly area itself is not impacting upon the natural or built environment. This is particularly the case if the site is run by a sub-contractor, who may be unaware of the conditions that have been imposed on the principal contractor.

Secondly, ensure that identified sensitive areas are adequately marked out and protected against potential damage through the restriction of movement of workers or plant and machinery. This will minimise any potential impact.

Seabirds, waterfowl, over-wintering birds and marine mammals are of significant importance in the coastal zone. Any works must take account of their breeding seasons and the times at which birds rest on land or congregate at sea. The timing of work is crucial in the avoidance of some impacts, such as disturbance and the abandonment of young. Contracts may stipulate conditions that avoid construction occurring during sensitive breeding periods and/or times of hard weather. It is extremely important that these conditions are rigorously observed and upheld.

Watch out on site

Site staff are not expected to be ecological experts. However, they are expected to be reasonably aware of potential problems and to seek training and/or advice if necessary.

Works affecting a SSSI

SSSIs are the primary UK designation (Areas of Special Scientific Interest (ASSI) in Northern Ireland), for protecting sites of national and international importance for nature conservation. An on-site staff member must be appointed as the primary contact with the relevant conservation agency if works are to be undertaken directly on or adjacent to a SSSI or NNR/MNR.

> Make sure that an agreement with the relevant conservation authority over working practices is in place before moving onto the site. If such an agreement is not acquired then you could find yourself accused of intentional or reckless damage and disturbance to SSSI features.

> If work is to be undertaken within or near to a nature reserve, national park, forest park or other similarly managed property, then please ensure that you contact the UK Headquarters of the relevant organisation. Ordnance Survey maps indicate the presence of such areas and also watch out for public notice boards and road signs marking their physical boundaries.

Please note that a site may be designated for its geological or geomorphological interest and may feature exposures of particular rock types, active geomorphological processes and/or be rich in fossils. If such a designation exists, contract conditions may stipulate strict working conditions or even restrictions to access to avoid damage or coverage.

Working near water

By definition, any works carried out in the coastal zone, or at sea, can be classed as working near water. All possible care should be taken to prevent the pollution of coastal waters or associated watercourses. Careful handling, storage and disposal of chemicals, oils and other fluids is essential (Sections 2.3.4 and 3.5.4).

Relevant issues include

- De-watering can have significant impacts upon coastal wetlands. Monitoring of water levels should be carried out regularly.

- Potential changes to local currents or areas of erosion/deposition should have already been identified. Works must be carried out in compliance with any special approaches that may have been highlighted.

Reinstating habitats

Measures to restore habitats damaged during construction works may form part of the contract or planning conditions. Such measures have to be planned in advance and will require the input of specialist advice. Restoring habitats in the marine environment is logistically more difficult than on land, due to the complexities, dynamics and sensitivities of the systems involved. Thorough planning is essential, although preventing damage, in the first instance, is always the preferred approach.

3.6.5 Dealing with key and protected animals

Birds

If birds are likely to be significantly disturbed by the works, then it would be advisable to amend the construction programme so as to avoid sensitive periods such as the breeding season and periods of extreme weather conditions. If works are to be carried out in an especially sensitive or designated area (ie a Special Protection Area (SPA)), then advice and permission should have been sought from the relevant nature conservation agency in advance of the works. Works should not proceed unless this consent is in place.

Nesting seabirds (eg little terns), and seals are protected during their breeding season, disturbing these animals is an offence. During construction, maintain checks around the site for these species and, if observed, seek advice from the relevant authorities.

Marine fauna

Whales, dolphins and porpoises ("cetaceans") are protected by UK, European and international legislation. It is an offence to deliberately disturb, injure or kill these animals.

 Dead or live stranded cetaceans should be reported immediately to either the Veterinary Investigation Centre at Inverness (01463 243030) for animals in Scotland or to the Cetaceans Stranding Coordinator at London Zoo (020 7449 6691) for animals in England and Wales. The Royal Society for the Prevention of Cruelty to Animals (RSPCA) (08705 555999) and Scottish SPCA (SSPCA) (0131 339 0111) should be contacted directly if the animal is still alive.

For further information on disturbance to marine fauna resulting from acoustic work, please refer to Section 3.2.3. JNCC is also available to advise on the preparation of Environmental Protection Plans for offshore operations. Further information can be obtained from its Senior Offshore Advisor in Aberdeen (01224 621488).

Seals present in UK waters are protected during their breeding season (September to January for Grey Seals and June to September for Common Seals) by the Conservation of Seals Act 1970. Under this Act it is an offence to kill, maim or injure seals in UK waters. Fines or custodial sentences can be imposed for deliberate killing or injuring.

 Sick, dead or injured seals should be reported immediately to the RSPCA in your region or the RSPCA Norfolk Wildlife Hospital (01553 842336) in England and Wales and the local SSPCA Inspector in Scotland.

Basking sharks are the largest UK fish (10–11 m long). They are commonly found in UK waters between April and September, especially around Western Scotland, the central Irish Sea and south western England. This species is protected both under national and international legislation, which makes harassment and deliberate killing an offence.

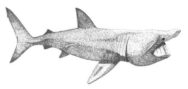

A basking shark

Any incidents involving a basking shark should be reported immediately to the Shark Trust, c/o the National Aquarium in Plymouth (01752 672008).

Turtles are commonly found off the west coast of Great Britain between August and October. All species are protected under both national and international legislation, but it is not an offence to help turtles if entangled or stranded, or to temporarily hold dead turtles for later examination by experts.

Further information on turtles, efforts to help protect the species and contact details for encounters can be found in the Marine Conservation Society's UK Turtle Code (2002).

In England and Wales, live strandings or entanglements must be reported directly to the RSPCA (08705 555999), SSPCA (0131 339 0111) in Scotland or, in Northern Ireland, to the Portrush Countryside Centre (07770 570350).

Biodiversity Action Plans and priority habitats and species

Three types of Biodiversity Action Plans have been developed within the UK, all of which set priorities for nationally important and locally important habitats and wildlife. They are:

- Species Action Plans
- Habitat Action Plan
- Local Biodiversity Action Plans.

Species Action Plans exist for species such as the basking shark, sea monkfish, the native oyster and sea squirts, amongst others. Action Plans define the current status of the species, the major pressures that are causing loss or decline, and objectives and targets for future conservation and management. **Habitat Action Plans** provide a summary descriptions of the key habitats found within the UK and the current issues encountered in their management and conservation. In the coastal and marine environment, the habitats covered include saltmarsh, sand dunes, vegetated shingle, maritime cliffs and slopes, mudflats and sublittoral sands and gravels. Around 160 **Local Biodiversity Action Plans** are in preparation or being implemented across Great Britain. Each Action Plan works on the basis of partnership to identify local priorities and to determine the contribution they can make to the delivery of the national Species and Habitat Action Plan targets. For more information on the above or to find out if any of the above Action Plans are relevant to your works or site, please contact your company's environmental representative and/or appropriate conservation agency or see www.ukbap.org.uk.

3.6.6 Physical damage to habitats and features

Sensitive habitats and important geological features can be significantly affected by construction works both directly and indirectly (in response to adjacent works eg downstream). Inappropriate works or badly managed procedures can damage natural features through:

- the crushing of soft sediments by heavy machinery

- the disruption of sediment supply due to the presence of temporary obstructions

- the erosion of features and habitat (ie sand dunes and inter tidal areas) through the movement of vehicles and the workforce, and through the transfer and storage of materials

- the change in context of a site due to significant and long-term damage.

Much of this damage can be avoided through improving the understanding of all site personnel as to the value of the habitat and features within which they are operating. If you are uncertain where work should be undertaken and/or are unaware of environmental sensitivities, contact the statutory conservation agency.

Robin Hood Bay

A condition was imposed on the contractors to replace boulders in their original positions on the foreshore given they contribute to the geological importance of the Robin Hood's Bay: Maw Wyke to Beast Cliff SSSI and candidate SAC. The photo (right) shows how rock armour was incorrectly placed at this intertidal site, outside of the area covered by planning permission conditions, causing damage to a valued geological SSSI. This demonstrates the need to identify dedicated officers to ensure there is effective enforcement of conditions.

West Sussex County Council produced guidelines for contractors when working on vegetated shingle, to help identify ways in which damage to these sensitive sites could be avoided. Shingle community identification "cab" cards were also produced. For more details visit www.pebbledash.org.uk

Raising operators' awareness and understanding

Damage to features, habitat or the loss of scientifically important objects (eg fossils) can be avoided by:

- explaining the importance of the site to staff

- establishing a code of good practice

- induction training of operators before works commence

- providing posters and signs identifying risks and good practice

- the maintenance of a watching brief, which may comprise the use of external paid or volunteer scientific expertise, or the conservation agency (ie a local conservation team member).

If in doubt as to the value or importance of features or objects discovered, contact the relevant conservation agency.

Contingency

There will be some sites where the potential for important geological finds (eg intact large vertebrate fossils), may be significant. Such eventualities may require that works cease or continue on other aspects of the development whilst excavation is undertaken. It may, therefore, be advisable to include a contingency plan for such an outcome and to take steps to determine the likelihood for such potential at an early stage in the development.

If access to the shore is necessary, disturbance should be minimised through the marking out of a clear working area with highly visible reflective tape. The size of the working area should be based upon the nature of the works themselves (ie the type of plant being used). For the workforce, an access area of 2 m would probably suffice, a larger area would be required for vehicular movement.

Geotextile mats can be lain down to minimise disturbance in certain habitats (ie saltmarsh). If working over rocky shores, consider laying sand over the shore and then laying geotextile over the top. This will help to protect the underlying rock and, over short periods, marine life can survive the covering.

3.6.7 Recognising problems and taking action

Careful planning and effective management on the construction site should ensure that damage to species and habitats is minimised. Where impacts do occur, they will be most visible through the following:

● discoloration, retreat of and visible damage to noted habitats in the area

● sick, injured or dead birds and/or fish in the vicinity of the site

● crushed plants, visible signs of trampling and vehicular damage to flora

● beached or stranded marine mammals

● disappearance of seaweeds and sedentary animals (ie limpets) from rocks in and around the site.

If you suspect that a protected plant or animal may be affected (ie unusual or abnormal behaviour, signs of distress – as detailed above), by your operations, stop and seek specialist advice before continuing.

> If multiple incidents of "bird-strike" (ie collision with infrastructure), are encountered on a new building or feature then you must contact the relevant conservation agency to seek advice on how to deal with this problem.

Clear signage to prevent pollution and damage to a SSSI

Designated sites

Sites of international importance

RAMSAR (UK is a signatory to this international convention)	Sites listed under the Convention on Wetlands of International Importance. These protected sites are of ecological importance particularly but not exclusively for waterfowl habitats. *UK Statutory Designation*: SSSI. *Contact*: The conservation agencies.
Special Protection Area (SPA)	Classified under the EC Directive on the Conservation of Wild Birds (the "Birds" Directive). *UK Statutory Designation*: (all SPAs are SSSIs). *Contact*: The conservation agencies.
Special Area of Conservation (SAC)	This site is classified under the EC Directive on the Conservation of Natural Habitats and Wild Flora and Fauna (the Habitats Directive). *UK Statutory Designation*: SAC (all SACs are European Marine Sites and SSSIs when above low water). *Contact*: The conservation agencies.

Sites of national importance

Sites of Special Scientific Interest (SSSI) or Area of Special Scientific Interest (ASSI)	Notified under Section 28 of the Wildlife and Countryside Act 1981 (as amended) and the Nature Conservation and Amenity Lands Orders 1985 respectively. These sites have been studied in detail; particular aspects of the site will be highlighted in the site schedule. *UK Statutory Designation*: SSSI/ASSI. *Contact*: The conservation agencies.
National Nature Reserves (NNR) and Marine Nature Reserves (MNR)	NNR/MNRs are managed primarily for nature conservation benefits. *UK Statutory Designation*: NNR/MNR. *Contact*: The conservation agencies.

Designated sites (cont)	
Sites of regional or local importance	
Local Nature Reserve (LNR)	A habitat of local significance that makes a contribution to nature conservation and to the opportunities for the public to enjoy wildlife. *UK Statutory Designation*: LNR. *Contact*: local authority.
Non-statutory nature reserves	These areas are established and managed by a variety of public and private bodies for specific ecological interest. *Contact*: County wildlife trusts, RSPB, the National Trust.
Sites of importance for nature conservation/key wildlife sites	Usually adopted by the local authority for planning purposes.The name and status of these sites can vary considerably.

3.6.8 Main legislation and key guidance

The Conservation (Natural Habitats &c) Regulations 1994 (as amended) (also known as the Habitat Regulations) and the Conservation (Natural Habitats, &c.) Regulations (Northern Ireland) 1995

These regulations formally transpose the requirements of the EC Habitats Directive into national law. They build on existing nature conservation legislation for the protection of habitats and species listed in the Directive and apply its considerations in respect of development control and pollution control legislation.

The Regulations provide for the creation of a network of protected areas across the UK consisting of Special Areas of Conservation (SAC) and Special Protection Areas (SPA), the latter of which are designated under the Birds Directive. These sites are part of a range of measures aimed at conserving important or threatened habitats and species. These important sites are identified for their fragile and sensitive ecosystems, meriting strict and in-depth examination of proposed developments prior to their construction.

Please note that all construction processes occurring within or near to a SAC or SPA will have been open to significant scrutiny and may be subject to rigid operating conditions to ensure that the integrity of the site is not affected. Due to the sensitivities of these sites, all works management and personnel should be made aware of the likely implications of impacts and the need to remain vigilant and conscious of potential risks. It is advisable to obtain contact details for the local conservation bodies and to maintain contact when undertaking potentially hazardous processes.

The Wildlife and Countryside Act 1981 (as amended)

The Wildlife and Countryside Act is the principle mechanism for the legislative protection of wildlife in Great Britain and the Act under which SSSIs are designated in England and Wales. It does not extend to Northern Ireland (covered by the Nature Conservation and Amenity Lands Orders 1985 (Northern Ireland)), the Channel Islands or the Isle of Man. The Countryside and Rights of Way Act (CROW) Act 2000 amended the Wildlife and Countryside Act. This represents a crucial piece of legislation and it is essential that all site staff are briefed on the associated responsibilities of undertaking work on or near to a SSSI.

> The CROW Act introduced new offences for anyone who damages, destroys or disturbs any of the features of interest for which the site was notified. It is essential that you:
>
> - adhere strictly to the conditions attached to a planning permission or consent, in order to maintain the wildlife interests for which the site has been designated
>
> - fully brief key site staff as to the sensitivity of the site and the conditions that have been put in place
>
> - identify a member of staff who can act as a primary contact for the statutory conservation authorities with whom conservation issues can be addressed.
>
> The CROW Act greatly strengthened both species and SSSI protection in England and Wales. Similar changes are likely for Scotland and Northern Ireland in the near future.

The Conservation of Seals Act 1970

The Conservation of Seals Act 1970 makes it a criminal offence to kill, maim or injure grey or common seals in British waters and establishes a general framework including times of year and methods in which seal killing is unlawful.

The Wild Mammals (Protection) Act 1996 (England, Wales and Scotland)

In addition to the protection offered to mammals under Part I of the Wildlife and Countryside Act, more general protection is offered under this Act. It is an offence for any person to mutilate, kick, beat, nail or otherwise impale, stab, burn, stone, crush, drown, drag or asphyxiate any wild mammal with the intent of inflicting unnecessary suffering.

Key guidance – wildlife and natural features

- RSPCA, Stranded whales, dolphins and porpoises – A first aid guide, 1992.

- Countryside Council for Wales (CCW), A Glossary of Marine Nature Conservation and Fisheries, 2001.

- English Nature, Sites of Special Scientific Interest (SSSIs), 2002.

- English Nature, Special Sites for Birds – What are they?, 1999.

- English Nature, Types of Coastal Habitat Re-creation, Science Series No.13), 1993.

- The Marine Conservation Society, The United Kingdom Turtle Code, 2002.

Shellfish and fish

3.7 Shellfish and fish

3.7.1 The importance of fisheries

Many coastal and open waters provide important spawning and nursery habitats for shellfish and fish, as well as migratory routes for fish, which in turn often support important local fishing industries that benefit local economies. Fisheries can be affected by a wide range of construction activities with effects on water quality being key along with other impacts including habitat loss, increased noise, light and vibration levels and pollution.

3.7.2 Fines and costs

Coastal and marine construction activities can significantly affect fisheries resources if uncontrolled and unmanaged. This is particularly the case in sensitive areas such as nursery and spawning grounds. In addition, estuarine areas may be used as migratory routes to rivers by species such as salmon, sea trout and shad. Should any damage occur to these resources, there may be a requirement for costly remedial works to mitigate the actual or perceived problems.

There is also likely to be a requirement for costly compensation if a fisherman's livelihood is shown to be affected as a result of any construction activity. In addition, many coastal waters support extensive shellfish beds that are protected by legislation governing water quality.

3.7.3 The main issues

Pollution incidents

Pollution incidents (ie the entry of a substance into the sea or a watercourse that may cause harm or damage to aquatic life), can affect fish populations and fisheries in a range of ways, depending on the pollutant. For example, organic pollutants can reduce dissolved oxygen concentrations leading to increased mortality, whilst hydrocarbons and heavy metals can reduce the value of fish catches through the tainting of flesh.

Noise and vibration

Noise and vibration can affect the natural behaviour of adult fish as well as potentially cause mortality. If levels become unacceptable, avoidance reactions may be exhibited until conditions return to those that existed prior to the commencement of construction activities. If these unacceptable levels last for a long period of time, access to spawning areas or feeding grounds may be affected. Juvenile fish are more susceptible to the effects of noise and vibration and have less ability to avoid affected areas due to their limited swimming ability. Shellfish are more likely to be affected than finfish given their more limited ability to move away from the affected area.

CIRIA Publication C584   127

Dredging activities

Dredging activities can affect fish either directly, through increased mortality (as finfish and shellfish are entrained by dredge machinery) and loss of habitat, or indirectly due to increased suspended solid loads and/or decreased dissolved oxygen concentrations. Increased suspended sediment levels can cause physical damage to fish through damage to gills and can reduce the ability of fish to locate prey items. Re-deposition of this suspended sediment can also have significant adverse impacts on shellfish beds, especially when levels of deposition are high.

Reduced access to commercial fishing areas

Any construction activity that requires plant to be moored in coastal or offshore areas could potentially inhibit the access of fisherman to their fishing grounds. The exact effect on commercial fishing activity will depend on the time of year in which restrictions occur. However, current pressures on fish stocks and changing market demands mean that the majority of inshore fishermen fish all year round, targeting different species at different times. Therefore, the effects of reduced access are likely to be felt to some extent by local inshore fisherman whenever construction takes place.

Reduced catches due to impacts of dredging and construction

The cumulative effects of dredging and construction, including reduced water quality, loss of habitats and increased noise and vibration can lead to reduced productivity in fisheries. Ultimately this can lead to reduced commercial catches and landings.

Dredging, by its nature, results in a change in the condition of the sea bed. For example, in areas where the sea bed contains notable amounts of clay, clay balls can form during the cutting and pumping processes of dredging. These balls have the potential to disrupt trawling activity by clogging nets. In sand and gravel environments, dredging can leave behind a more sandy ridged sea bed. Other construction activities can also change the suitability of the seabed for trawling, including the loss of rock from barges during transfer; the illegal disposal of waste materials (ie piping, plastics etc) by site staff directly into the sea; and the sterilisation of grounds by the actual placement of materials (eg dredged clay) or through the location of the works themselves (eg reclamation).

3.7.4 Avoiding problems

General

The protection of fisheries can be achieved through the simple adoption of general good practice and site management. In addition to those measures already detailed in preceding sections, the following are recommended for adoption on-site.

Noise levels should be minimised as far as possible (as detailed in Section 3.2.4). Particular attention should be paid to shellfish areas, where the ability of the these species to move away from the noise source may be limited.

If noise impacts persist for long enough, fish may stay away from spawning areas and eventually will not spawn at all.

The risk of pollution incidents should be minimised and avoided through the use of the measures detailed in Section 3.5.4. Protective measures should be in place to prevent spills from entering the sea or the local drainage system. If water is polluted during a spill then it should be contained, removed and disposed of as quickly as possible (ie following guidelines laid out in Section 3.5.5 of this guide).

The timing and location of construction activity should be planned with consideration for critical times of the year (spawning/migration period) and sensitive locations (spawning areas) for any existing species. This can be particularly relevant where the works involve dredging.

Commercial fisheries

For large-scale projects, it is good practice to appoint a fisheries liaison officer prior to any construction activities beginning. Examples of projects where such a position is advantageous include major dredging operations, coastal defence works, port, harbour and marina construction and offshore developments (windfarms, oil exploration). It is usually the responsibility of the developer to organise and fund this position. In many instances, local fishing organisations will recommend trained individuals who can fulfil the duties of this position. These duties should include:

- acting as the main contact between the contractor and the local fishing community during both the pre-construction and actual construction phases
- consulting and dealing with issues raised by the local fishing community
- informing local fisherman of the nature, extent and location of construction activities, including dredging
- informing local fisherman of possible access restrictions
- consulting local fisherman on dredging strategies to ensure that areas recognised as important fishing grounds are avoided as far as possible
- liasing with DEFRA Fishery Officers in England and Local Sea Fisheries Committee Officers in England and Wales; the Department for Agriculture for Northern Ireland; and the General Manager of the Scottish Fishermens' Federation (Aberdeen).

In addition to this, it is often advisable to notify members of the local fishing industry of any planned significant construction works by placing public notices in industry publications such as Fishing News (published weekly).

3.7 Shellfish and fish

3.7.5 Recognising impacts and taking action

Daily inspections should be made for visible signs of fish distress and/or mortality. If identified, appropriate counter-measures should be taken to determine and then rectify the problem.

Emergency response

Should a pollution incident occur which is unable to be contained on-site, then the relevant environment agency should be contacted on 0800 807060 for coastal waters; and the Maritime and Coastguard Agency (24-hour Infoline 0870 6006505) when the incident is at sea. In addition to these organisations, the local Sea Fisheries Committee Officer and DEFRA Fishery Officer should also be informed so that they can inform the local fishing industry. For more information see Section 3.5.5.

3.7.6 Main legislation and key references

Directly applicable legislation includes

- **Salmon and Freshwater Fisheries Act 1975 (England and Wales)** states that is an offence to pollute waters containing fish so as to cause the waters to be poisonous or injurious to fish, their food or spawning grounds.

- **Shellfish Waters Directive** (79/923/EEC) – implemented in Great Britain under the Shellfish Waters (Shellfish) (Classifications) Regulations 1997 (also in Northern Ireland under separate legislation). This legislation requires the designation of shellfish waters and sets requirements for water quality such that the waters contribute to the quality of shellfish for human consumption.

- **EC Shellfish Hygiene Directive** (91/492/EEC) – implemented in Great Britain under the Food Safety (Fishery Products and Live Shellfish) (Hygiene) Regulations 1998 (also in Northern Ireland under separate legislation). This legislation monitors and regulates flesh quality.

Other related legislation includes

- **Environmental Protection Act 1990 (England, Scotland and Wales)** which defines noise (including vibration) emanating from premises, which is prejudicial to health or is a nuisance, as a statutory nuisance and places controls on waste management, including a "duty of care".

- **Water Resources Act 1991 (England and Wales)** states that is an offence to cause or knowingly permit any matter which is itself polluting or has a polluting effect to enter controlled waters (ie watercourses, groundwater or coastal marine waters). The Control of Pollution Act (1974 and amendments) in Scotland has the same provisions (SEPA).

CIRIA Publication C584

- **The Control of Pollution Act 1974** exercises controls on noise and vibration from construction activities in Great Britain.

> **Key guidance – shellfish and fish**
>
> - Health and Safety Executive Regulations/Guidance.
> - BS 5228 (Part 1 1987 – Basic information and procedures for noise control).
> - Construction (Design Management) Regulations 1994.
> - English Nature, Good practice guidelines for ports and harbours operating within or near UK European Marine Sites, July 1999.

3.8 Archaeology and heritage

3.8.1 The importance of protecting archaeology and heritage

The coastal and marine environment holds the preserved remains of many features of historic interest which represent human activity and settlement over the past 10 000 years. Much of this "archaeological resource" is found at sea (eg wrecks and other maritime structures), and other rare remains, such as bronze and iron age finds, can also be found in the coastal environment. These remains are an irreplaceable and finite resource, which lose much of their value when removed. Archaeological sites and features form a backdrop to our national heritage and the historic development of the country, as well as international developments in trade, industry, shipbuilding, etc.

Many archaeological remains are protected by legislation, such as those detailed in Section 3.8.6. All of these acts protect (to some degree) the archaeological resource in the coastal and marine environment, however, the protection generally extends beyond those sites already designated.

> **Heritage bodies**
>
> - **English Heritage:** conserves and enhances the historic environment, increases the understanding of the past and broadens access and appreciation of the heritage in England.
> - **Historic Scotland:** Safeguards the nation's built heritage and promotes its understanding and enjoyment.
> - **CADW (Welsh Historic Monuments):** conserves, protects and presents the built heritage of Wales and undertakes the Secretary of State's statutory responsibilities for securing all ancient monuments for the future.
> - **The Environment and Heritage Service:** protects and conserves the natural and built environment and promotes its appreciation for the benefit of present and future generations in Northern Ireland.

3.8.2 Fines and costs

If a designated wreck, military craft, Scheduled Ancient Monument (SAM), or Listed Building is located within the area where works are being undertaken, and is physically disturbed or damaged, prosecution resulting in a fine can occur. Furthermore, work at the site would have to stop whilst an evaluation of the damage is undertaken. The requirement to make good the damage caused by the works may be part of the prosecution.

In the event that non-designated sites/features are discovered, works would also have to cease in order for an evaluation of the value of the finds to be made. Therefore, the discovery of any archaeological remains could have significant impacts on the timing and duration of works.

3.8.3 The main causes of problems and incidents

The following are the main causes of incidents relating to archaeological remains:

- Planning conditions or specified working methods (or an awareness of the potential for finds) are not passed down from client to contractor. This can result in the breaking of conditions or the use of construction methods that disturb or damage the archaeological interests.

- Designated sites/wrecks or listed buildings are not identified and demarcated, which result in vehicles or works in areas of designated interest.

- Secondary effects of the works are not incorporated into impacts (eg vibration impacts on listed buildings or SAMs, and drawdown of water levels due to dewatering on sensitive sites).

- The assumption that if there are no known archaeological remains then there must be none! Thus, no systems are in place to recognise or report any remains, and no measures exist to prevent finds disrupting works.

> Where possible, the preferred option for dealing with archaeological sites is in-situ preservation, rather than excavation. Historical sites are a finite resource that should be left untouched. Please note that excavation can be expensive and time-consuming.

3.8.4 Avoiding problems

In order to avoid problems relating to the archaeological resource, the following should be undertaken prior to the commencement of works on-site:

- The client should be asked for all details regarding the site in terms of pre-construction evaluation, which may include ES, planning conditions, consultation and any other information held by the client. This will enable all known aspects of the site to be planned for within the working methodology.

- All designated sites that are identified from the above should be clearly marked out prior to commencement of works, and all site-staff must be instructed to avoid these areas unless excavation is part of the agreed works.

- Where a specific working methodology is required, all appropriate site staff should be informed at the start of works and immediately prior to undertaking these aspects.

- Where new or unforeseen activities are required, appropriate advice should be sought to ascertain the potential archaeological implications. This may also require consultation with the local authority or other relevant bodies (eg English Heritage).

- Prior to commencement of the works a member of the site-staff should be identified as the initial contact regarding archaeological interests. This member of staff should be aware of the problems, sources of advice, and requirements under legislation (see Section 3.8.6), in case of finds or disturbance to existing structures.

- If the potential for archaeological resource exists in an area, then appropriate plans should be in place prior to commencement of the works, establishing procedures should a discovery be made. This may include phasing of works, the identification of specific working areas and compartmentalisation.

- Furthermore, should the potential for finds exist, an archaeological watching brief should be maintained. This is often nominated and co-ordinated by the local authority archaeologist.

Variations in the scheme design or the works during construction may have unpredictable effects on the historic environment. This is because areas outside of the original groundworks may not have been evaluated as to their archaeological potential in pre-construction studies. If variations are necessary, please contact your local authority and relevant heritage body for advice on how to proceed.

3.8 Archaeology and heritage

3.8.5 Action to take

Problems regarding the archaeological resource can be identified only through monitoring. There are several ways that monitoring can be undertaken on-site and a number of applicable actions in the following circumstances:

All known archaeological sites within the working area should be fenced off, and the fencing inspected frequently to ensure that it is a) still standing and visible, and b) not disturbed.

Action: any fencing or visible markings around a designated site should be maintained in good visual order. Where the fencing has been disturbed, an inspection should be made by the site manager to determine whether any potential damage has occurred to the designated site/structure. If damage is believed to have taken place, the local authority archaeologist should be contacted if the structure is a listed building. If the structure is a SAM, English Heritage, CADW, Historic Scotland or the Northern Ireland Environment and Heritage Service should be contacted.

Where specific working methods are in force, the site manager should ensure that, for specific activities, they are being correctly implemented.

Action: the site manager should monitor through routine checks that the correct working methods are being used. If unsuitable methods (ie breaching planning conditions or a methodology agreed upon with the heritage authority), are being used, works should cease and the local authority archaeologist should be contacted to enable assessment of any potential damage.

If there is not a requirement for an archaeological watching brief, site staff should be made aware that any sightings of artefacts, particularly wood, metals, bricks, stone fragments, tile, pottery, coins, skeletons, or burned and blackened material, could indicate the presence of archaeological remains.

Action: All site-staff associated with disturbance works should be informed of the need to be aware of potential archaeological finds and provided with a contact (eg site manager), in the event of finds being discovered.

If artefacts or historical features are identified during disturbance works.

Action: work should cease immediately and the area marked out to avoid further disturbance. The on-site archaeological contact should be informed and should examine the finds before obtaining specialist advice. The local planning authority archaeologist should also be contacted. If an archaeological specialist is employed by the contractor/client, mitigation measures may be agreed quickly with the local authority archaeologist. The local authority archaeologist may also require contact with the heritage bodies, such as English Heritage, particularly in the case of a wreck being encountered.

Archaeology and heritage 3.8

If coins or other valuable metals are revealed; if the finds are found in the foreshore and they are not Treasure Trove, they are owned by the landowner of the foreshore.

Action: work should cease immediately and the area marked out to avoid further disturbance works. The on-site archaeological contact should then be informed and they should inspect the finds and take advice from the local authority archaeologist. The local coroner and the British Museum should be contacted in order for a determination of whether the find is Treasure Trove.

If skeletons are revealed.

Action: work should cease immediately and the area marked out to avoid further disturbance. The police should be informed immediately, in order to examine the finds, as well as the on-site archaeological contact who should also inform the local authority archaeologist. If the remains are human skeleton, the Police will determine the methodology for their removal in conjunction, as appropriate, with the local authority archaeologist.

Treasure trove

The Treasure Act 1996 – The following finds are defined as treasure under the Act:

- any object other than a coin provided that it contains at least 10 per cent of gold or silver and is at least 300 years old when found.

- all coins from the same find provided they are at least 300 years old when found.

- any object, whatever it is made of, that is found in the same place as, or that had previously been together with, another object that is treasure.

- any object that would previously have been treasure trove, but does not fall within the specific categories given above.

These objects have to be made substantially of gold or silver; they have to have been buried with the intention of recovery and their owner or his heirs cannot be traced. The following types of find are not treasure:

- objects whose owners can be traced

- unworked natural objects including human and animal remains, even if they are found in association with treasure

- objects from the foreshore which are wreck.

Always report your find to the relevant heritage body or local authority archaeologist.

3.8.6 Main legislation and key references

Burials Act 1857 (England and Wales)

This act makes it necessary for a licence to be obtained to remove human burials or human remains. Conditions can be issued with the licence for the removal and disposal of the remains by an archaeologist.

Merchant Shipping Act 1894 (England, Wales and Northern Ireland)

Under this act, there is a requirement to inform the Receiver of Wrecks of any finds removed from wreckage. This act covers the sea up to High Water Spring Tide and applies to all material landed in a UK port.

Protection of Wrecks Act 1973 (England, Wales and Northern Ireland)

Under this act, the relevant heritage bodies have the power to designate wrecks around the UK. The designation results in a protective zone around the wreck and no disturbance can be undertaken within this area without consent.

Ancient Monuments and Archaeological Areas Act 1979 (England, Wales and Scotland)

Under this act, English Heritage, CADW and Historic Scotland can designate structures and features as being "Scheduled", which prevents disturbance or damage to the structure and its visual surroundings from any new activities.

Any works to or immediately adjacent to a SAM must have Scheduled Monument Consent (SMC) from the Secretary of State. SMC may set requirements to limit damage to the SAM, which must be implemented during construction. Unauthorised damage to a SAM is a criminal offence.

Protection of Military Remains Act 1986 (England, Wales and Scotland)

This act enables all British military remains to be protected (ie no disturbance activities can be undertaken). The act extends this protection beyond territorial waters where the disturbance is carried out by a British citizen or from a British controlled vessel. This act enables remains to be protected without their position being known.

Town and Country Planning Act 1990 (England and Wales)

Under this act, local authorities can protect a wide range of archaeological remains, by requiring investigations prior to development or imposing planning conditions on-site.

The Planning (Listed Buildings and Conservation Areas) Act 1990 (England and Wales)

This enables local authorities to compile a list of buildings or structures of special, architectural or historic interest. This ensures the protection of the structure, and disturbance works to the structure would require listed building consent.

Archaeology and heritage **3.8**

- Planning Policy Guidance 16 Archaeology and Planning (1996) – this document sets out best practice for incorporating archaeology and heritage issues within planning permissions (Policy Planning Guidance 16 in England and Wales; National Planning Policy Guidance 5 in Scotland).

- Consultation with heritage bodies (English Heritage, CADW, Historic Scotland and the Northern Ireland Environment and Heritage Service).

- Department for Culture, Media and Sport, The Treasure Act (leaflet), 1997.

- English Heritage and CADW, Marine Aggregate Dredging and the Historic Environment, (produced by the British Marine Aggregate Producers Association (BMAPA) for English Heritage and CADW.

4 Construction processes

4.1 Demolition

Introduction

At every stage of the construction process (including post-operational maintenance and re-construction activities), there is the potential for environmental damage. This chapter highlights the issues that site staff need to be aware of, and to plan for, during a number of construction processes.

The chapter has a similar format to the existing CIRIA guide, *Environmental good practice on site* (C502), and concentrates on the 17 most common construction processes undertaken at the coast and in marine areas. Material already presented in C502 is not repeated here, but is cross-referenced, where appropriate.

Key issues for each of the construction processes are sub-divided into contractual issues (should be in place before arriving on site), and construction issues (to be considered during works). Contractual issues are most relevant to works where consents and permits have not been acquired or where conditions that have been established affect construction itself.

In all cases, be aware of the permits and consents that may have been required as part of the design and planning of the development (see various Sections within Chapter 3). Always check for their existence and be aware of stipulated conditions.

> Further information on the types of issues and impacts that may arise from individual development types can be found in the Environment Agency "Scoping Guidelines for the Environmental Impact Assessment of Projects: Guidance Notes". www.environment-agency.gov.uk

4.1 Demolition

Key issues – Demolition	Refer to
Contractual Issues	
Check your contract and consent documents (as appropriate). What working conditions have been established for demolition activities, if any? If you are uncertain or if a particular issue does not seem to have been covered, contact client and/or the local authority.	Setting up and managing site, 2.3 Waste, 3.1.3 and 3.1.6

Key issues – Demolition (cont)	Refer to

Construction Issues

Before demolition begins, review the disposal options for the materials that will be generated. Because of the large quantities and transport distances often associated with materials, use the following waste hierarchy, as far as possible, in preference to disposal (see also Dredging and Excavation):

Waste (storage and disposal), 3.1.4
Dredging , 4.2
Excavation, 4.3

1. Re-use materials on-site.
2. Send materials to be reclaimed or recycled in the locality.
3. Send materials by sea or rail to be reclaimed or recycled further afield.
4. Send materials by road to be reclaimed or recycled further afield.

Road haulage for disposal may be necessary in some cases but access to coastal sites can be restricted and/or along narrow roads. The whole process can add additional road traffic hazard, be visually intrusive, and generate noise, vibration, dust and undesirable emissions. If road haulage is essential, then various measures can be utilised to minimise effects on the environment.

Noise and vibration, 3.2.4
Dust, emissions and odours, 3.3.3
Traffic, 2.3.5

For example, wheel washing facilities can be employed to avoid contamination of road surfaces, and the covering of wagons or the spraying of water over crushed materials will help to prevent dust. Also, consider using marine plant as an alternative to land-based plant and haulage. This is potentially less costly with less environmental impact (including lower greenhouse gas emissions), but note that 24-hour operation is common.

Noise and vibration can disrupt your neighbours social and commercial activities. Avoid noisy sorting operations on site or at high physical elevation. Consider localised screening of the noisy operation or, subject to other constraints, carry out sorting operations at lower elevations (eg on the foreshore) or off site. When working tides, try to organise noisy operation for day shifts (but note that times of low tides may not permit this).

Noise and vibration, 3.2.4

4.2 Dredging

Key issues – Demolition (cont)	Refer to
Dust presents increased health risks for local residents and discourages tourists and visitors alike. It may also damage (ie by smothering), coastal ecology. Control it by damping down stockpiles in dry windy conditions and screening. If concrete or masonry materials are to be crushed on site, check that the necessary licences have been obtained from the local Environment Health Officer.	Dust, emissions and odours, 3.3.3
Follow other good practice for crushing operations, removing/perforating tanks, dust control, and use of elephant chutes.	CIRIA C502
Dispose of any materials in accordance with your Duty of Care, segregating out any pollutants.	
Be aware of potential archaeological discoveries during demolition activities (ie remains and artefacts).	Archaeology and heritage, 3.8.5

4.2 Dredging

Key issues – Dredging (cont)	Refer to
Contractual Issues	
Waste: disposal of dredgings on land.	Waste (storage and disposal), 3.1.4
Ensure that any permissions required under Waste Management Licensing Regulations (1994) are in place, as dredged materials may contain contaminants. Check whether there are any conditions attached to the permission that set restrictions on dredging. If not in place, plan early to allow time to obtain them.	Ground and sediment contamination, 3.4.4
Potential for risk of contamination of dredgings, such as oils and heavy metals. Sample sediments as required.	Special Waste Regulations 1996.
Aim to reuse the dredged material (for example, to improve agricultural land or for flood defence/nourishment applications) rather than disposing to landfill.	Waste (storage and disposal) 3.1.4

Key issues – Dredging (cont)	Refer to
Waste: disposal of dredging, at sea.	Waste (storage and disposal), 3.1.4
In England, Wales and Scotland, disposal of dredged material at sea requires a Food and Environment Protection Act (FEPA) (1985) licence. This is obtainable from your national environmental department and may take substantial time to acquire, based on the complexity of the project. This licence may impose operational restrictions, such as:	

i. Time of year disposal can take place.

ii. Quantities that can be disposed of over a particular timescale.

iii. Restrictions for materials from certain areas.

iv. Fishing liaison arrangements to minimise disruption.

v. Conditions relating to proposed methods.

vi. Ensuring that damage/disruption of habitats is kept to a minimum.

vii. Ensure turbidity is kept to a prescribed level.

| Ensure that a discharge consent (from the relevant environment agency) for returning effluent from de-watering dredgings to controlled waters has been obtained. If an EIA or EAP has been undertaken for the dredging operations, acquaint yourself with the potential impacts that were identified and the mitigation measures put forward to minimise or avoid them. Permission is required from the owner of the sea bed (ie the Crown Estate). | Shellfish and fish, 3.7.4
Wildlife and natural features, 3.6.7
Water quality, 3.5.4 |

Construction Issues

| Impact on aquatic ecology due to re-suspension of sediments and sediment plumes. | Shellfish and fish, 3.7.4 |
| Use an appropriate dredging technique to minimise the disturbance of sediment resulting in siltation of the water column and potential mobilisation of contaminants. The appropriate technique will have been identified in pre-construction design and planning studies. If, however, excessive levels of turbidity and/or changes in sediment deposition occur the method may need to be revised. | Shellfish and fish, 3.7.4 |

Key issues – Dredging (cont)	Refer to
Sediment plumes can also be minimised through the optimisation of trailing/cutting speeds and pump/suction discharge rates, limiting overflow, reducing water intake and using return flow, and shielding the cutter suction head.	
Consider using dredge mats (although the use and success of these will need to be discussed with specialists beforehand). Disturbance of organic silts and dying weed may give rise to deoxygenation. Monitor and aerate if necessary.	
Odour problems may arise from the sediments as they de-water.	Dust, emissions and odours, 3.3.3
Noise problems may be encountered as 24-hour working is common with dredging operations. However, these can be mitigated by, for example, the covering of pipelines and avoidance of supporting operations (eg dozing of deposited material during the night-time).	Noise and vibration, 3.2.4
High levels of noise may be generated by working with compacted sediments. Mechanical de-watering and compaction may lead to vibration.	Noise and vibration, 3.2.4
Navigation plant issues are discussed in Section 4.16.	Marine vessels and plant, 4.16
Be aware of the potential for the presence of unexploded ordnance in your area of works. If ordnance is discovered, contact the emergency services immediately.	
During dredging operations, respect the protection of any geological features agreed as a result of prior agreement/consultation with relevant conservation agency. Observe and adhere to traffic routing measures and restricted areas at all times, particularly in or near to habitats noted for their environmental fragility or sensitivity.	
Some dredging operations, particularly in estuaries and ports, can lead to archaeological finds. Ensure implementation of any appropriate measures to identify and preserve archaeological relics. In particularly sensitive cases this may entail having an on-board archaeologist (ie in the vicinity of wreck sites).	Archaeology and heritage, 3.8.5

4.3   Excavation

General guidance on onshore (ie above Extreme High Water Levels), excavations can be found in CIRIA C502, Sections 4.8 and 4.9. However, to enable the excavation operations below or near to water level to be carried out in dry conditions or to carry out other works, it may be necessary to construct temporary works. Each form of temporary works has its own environmental considerations in addition to the excavation itself (ie noise, dust etc). The potential effects of temporary works are discussed below.

Key issues – Excavation below/near water level	Refer to
Contractual Issues	
Check your contract and consent documents (as appropriate). What working conditions have been established for excavation activities, if any? If you are uncertain or if a particular issue has not been covered, contact client and/or the local authority. If excavation is below the low water mark, an FEPA licence should be in place. Check conditions, as appropriate.	Dredging, 4.2 Ground and sediment contamination, 3.4
Construction Issues	
Cofferdams	
Refer to guidance below on permanent piling. In addition, temporary works piles may well be second-hand and should be checked for any contaminants adhering to surfaces. There will inevitably be a requirement to maintain a pumping regime and the water discharge should be dealt with as for land discharges.	Pilling, 4.10 Water quality, 3.5.4 CIRIA C502, 3.1
De-watering	
Generally, discharged water from a wellpoint system will be clean, as it is drawn from the water table below ground. However, in the initial set up and draw down there is likely to be potential for discoloration and possible contamination. Other forms of de-watering using submersible pumps can generate more sediment and other contamination. Where this is likely to be significant, route water via a settlement area/tank with a physical filter (eg a rock bund), before returning to controlled waters. A consent from the relevant environment agency may be required in advance of making the discharge.	Water quality, 3.5.4

4.4 Drilling and blasting underwater

Key issues – Excavation (cont)	Refer to
Bunds	
Bunds are normally formed of graded rock and/or general fill material in a similar manner to a breakwater. However, upon completion of permanent works the bund will require removal and this may prove to be an arduous task (ie ensuring that all temporary material has been adequately removed). A pre- and post-bund construction survey may be required to demonstrate total removal. This may also lead to the requirement for diver inspections and directions for the removal of rock etc.	Rockworks, 4.8
Be aware of the potential for the presence of unexploded ordnance in your area of works. If ordnance is discovered, contact the emergency services immediately.	
Be aware of potential archaeological discoveries during excavation activities (ie remains and artefacts).	Archaeology and heritage, 3.8.5

4.4 Drilling and blasting underwater

Key issues – Drilling and blasting underwater	Refer to
Contractual Issues	
Plan and co-ordinate blasting operations to avoid fish spawning periods. This should have been established in your contract conditions. If it has not or you are uncertain about shellfish and fish sensitivity in your area, contact the relevant authorities.	Wildlife and natural features, 3.6.7 Shellfish and fish, 3.7.4
Before undertaking underwater drilling and blasting operations licences are required from the Police (to purchase and store or use explosives) and the Health and Safety Executive (HSE) (a Recipient Competent Authority (RCA) Licence also required for the purchase of explosives).	

Installation of pipelines and cables **4.5**

Key issues – Drilling and blasting underwater	Refer to
Construction issues	
Check and dispose of any unexploded charges used as part of blasting operations.	
Examine, disseminate and adhere to guidance on good practice. See below	

Key guidance – Drilling and blasting underwater
• The Marine Technology Directorate Ltd., Guidelines for the Safe Use of Explosives Under Water, MTD Publication 96/101. 1996.

4.5   Installation of pipelines and cables

Key issues – Pipelines and cables	Refer to
Contractual Issues	
Remember to plan ahead considering need for permissions – including licences to construct, to dispose of dredged material, to discharge (if applicable) etc. Check your contract and consent documents (as appropriate). What working conditions have been established for installation activities, if any? If you are uncertain or if a particular issue has not been covered, contact client and/or the local authority.	Dredging, 4.2 Water quality, 3.5.4 Waste (storage and disposal), 3.1.4
Construction issues	
Installation will require 24-hour working so noise may be an issue. Work should be timed so as to avoid sensitive seasons for wildlife and tourism etc. Though selection of working time will be dependent on weather so summer working may be inevitable.	Noise and vibration, 3.2.4
Placement or movement of materials and plant over sensitive habitats (ie mud flats) may have significant impact. Ensure that plant and workforce are	Wildlife & natural features, 3.6.7
(1) Aware of sensitivity.	
(2) Kept away from these areas.	

4.6 Nourishment and reclamation

Key issues – Pipelines and cables (cont)	Refer to
Construction works will dissect the beach and prevent access along it. Other activities such as watersports and swimming will also be disrupted. Navigation may also be affected during placement activities.	
Be aware of potential archaeological discoveries during operations (ie remains and artefacts).	Archaeology and heritage, 3.8.5

4.6 Nourishment and reclamation

Key issues – Nourishment and reclamation	Refer to
Contractual Issues	
Check your contract and consent documents (as appropriate). What working conditions have been established for activities, if any? If you are uncertain or if a particular issue has not been covered, contact your client and/or the relevant authority.	
Disruption to fishing may occur as a result of coastal and marine nourishment and reclamation operations (ie interruption of navigation, fishing, restriction of entry to fishing grounds). This can be avoided or mitigated against by addressing the problem early on in the planning process and by liasing with all interested parties. Of key importance is the need to maintain communication once construction activities have commenced. Raising awareness of operations and project progress can be undertaken through methods such as newsletters, telephone hotlines and on-site representation and/or notice boards.	Shellfish and fish, 3.7.4 Traffic, 2.3.5 Awareness, 2.3.1
Construction Issues	
Ensure all operations (both temporary stockpiling and final placing) conserve wildlife, habitats (including fisheries) and natural features as far as possible and as agreed.	Wildlife and natural features, 3.6.6
Need to ensure that relevant extraction licences are in place for the proposed filling material. Where possible make use of every opportunity for the beneficial use of dredged material.	

Nourishment and reclamation 4.6

Key issues – Nourishment and reclamation (cont)	Refer to
Grading, filling and compacting operations (eg for beaches), can generate high levels of noise. As such, consider possible screening of activities or timing to avoid more sensitive periods (ie bird use, anti-social hours etc).	
If being carried out hydraulically, then the operation should progress 24 hours a day to be economic. This will potentially result in complaints from local residents and businesses (if appropriate), with regard to noise pollution, if left unabated.	Noise and vibration, 3.2.4
Again, early consultation and effective mitigation may prevent unnecessary damage (ie screening, notice boards, newsletters etc).	
Dependent on the characteristics of the local area, restrictions may be set as to working days (ie weekends) or certain processes (ie noisy grading operations/techniques).	
Ensure fill being used is not contaminated and avoid pollution of waters, wildlife, habitats fisheries and natural features by sediment from filling.	Water quality, 3.5.4 Wildlife and natural features, 3.6.7
Such protection should include appropriate physical containment to avoid loss of deleterious small material.	Dust, emissions and odours, 3.3.3 Ground and sediment contamination, 3.4.4
Protect archaeological finds that may arise from the filling source.	Archaeology and heritage, 3.8.5
When covering sensitive geology, ensure that the appropriate measures, agreed with the relevant conservation agency, are properly implemented on site.	Wildlife and natural features, 3.6.6
When recharging sandy beaches note the potential for sand to liquefy and ensure appropriate safety precautions are taken.	

4.7 Geotextiles

Key guidance – Nourishment and reclamation
• *Beaches and Sand Dunes* – SEPA guide.
• *Beach management manual*, CIRIA R153, 1996.

4.7 Geotextiles

Key issues – Geotextiles	Refer to
Construction Issues	
Waste: dealing with packaging. Rolls are commonly wrapped in plastic sheaths which are often discarded in the haste to lay the geotextile (and similarly the central cardboard tube). A regime to collect and secure these items is required to avoid litter being scattered and lost through wind and wave action.	Waste (storage and disposal), 3.1.4
Waste: dealing with off-cuts from the ends of rolls. Off-cuts should be adequately collected and secured in containers or covered skips.	Waste (storage and disposal), 3.1.4

4.8 Rock works and placement of concrete units

Rock armour is normally delivered to construction sites in the UK by sea and from another country (eg Norway, France, Ireland). The alternative to the above is to use aggregate quarries in the UK and to supply the site by road. Theoretically, it would also be possible to open a dedicated quarry but there will be serious concerns over material quality and yield, as well as implications for the local environment. Please note that this is an issue that will have been dealt with in the design/planning phase.

Key issues – Rock works	Refer to
Construction Issues	
Many principles applicable to nourishment and reclamation are also relevant to rock works.	Nourishment and reclamation, 4.6
Temporary placement of rocks on seabed or foreshore: Rock brought to sites by sea may be discharged from the vessel using side tipping facilities or an on-board excavator. Ensure that wildlife, habitats (including fisheries), natural features and archaeological heritage are not affected by this process, and that navigation safety is preserved.	Wildlife and natural features, 3.6.6 Shellfish and fish, 3.7.4

CIRIA Publication C584

Rock works and placement of concrete units 4.8

Key issues – Rock works (cont)	Refer to
If rock or similar material is being brought to the site by sea it is frequently necessary to tranship material from a larger vessel (eg 20 000 tonne barge) to a smaller capacity shallow draft vessel (eg 1000 to 1500 tonne). This transhipment operation should be carried out with great care to avoid the loss of material which will inevitably need recovering. Such overboard material might be a future obstruction to the construction operation and to general navigation traffic in the area. It can also damage sensitive seabed ecology and certain marine habitats, and interfere with fishing activities.	Wildlife and natural features, 3.6.6 Shellfish and fish, 3.7.4
Temporary storage of rock and fill materials: where transhipping of rock is not possible it may be prudent to construct a temporary offloading facility that can be serviced at all states of the tide. The bund/jetty can be part of the permanent works to begin with, and then be removed and incorporated into the works after the final delivery.	Wildlife and natural features, 3.6.6 Shellfish and fish, 3.7.4
The delivery can be quickly offloaded during one high tide by block tipping over the edge of the jetty and on the following low tide an excavator retrieves the rock for placing in the works.	
Ensure that wildlife, habitats (including fisheries), natural features and archaeological heritage are not affected by this process, and that navigation safety is preserved.	
Vibration – road truck deliveries: where large volumes of rock are required, delivery by road is generally not an option.	Noise and vibration, 3.2.4
Local authorities recognise the potential for significant traffic congestion (invariably at peak periods), and the safety risk to the public and local infrastructure of rocks falling off during delivery.	
Dust on rock armour can cause plumes of discoloration.	Dust, emissions and odours, 3.3.3

4.8

Rock works and placement of concrete units

Key issues – Rock works (cont)	Refer to

Generally when rock is delivered by sea, any dust on the stone will have been washed off en route.

However, there may be dust or smaller material in the excavator buckets which could cause discoloration when placed in water. The operator should ensure that the bucket is emptied on shore prior to picking up the next load.

Safety problems can arise from failed ordnance originating from quarrying activities. This can occur as, occasionally, explosive charges may fail to detonate. This is evident when exposed wires coming out of the drilled shot holes are visible. Upon finding such wires or charges, the area should be cleared and the local police advised. They in turn will contact the bomb disposal unit to deal with the problem.

Construction Issues

Amenity of the coastline/beach for tourism and recreation will be significantly affected during the construction of rock works. Mitigate the impact of this as far as possible and consistent with safety.

Construction jobs can have a sightseeing potential in their own right and good information boards and leaflets are desirable.

Key issues – Precast concrete units	Refer to

Construction Issues

For on-site pre-casting follow good practice procedures for concrete batching, pours . and aftercare	CIRIA C502, Sections 4.4 and 4.5
To mitigate against any emissions, use shutter oils that are biodegradable and environmentally friendly.	Dust, emissions and odours, 3.3.3
Waste: Try to completely remove and properly dispose of shutters, PVC and casting membranes etc. Coastal sites are very windy and these materials tend to blow about and get into the water, causing an unsightly mess as well as potential ecological damage.	Waste (storage and disposal), 3.1.4

CIRIA Publication C584

Timber works 4.9

Key issues – Precast concrete units	Refer to
Waste: any surplus concrete, in the pre-cast yard, should be stockpiled, recycled and reused by crushing and screening as in 4.2 above.	Waste (storage and disposal), 3.1.4
Waste can occasionally arise during placing of pre-cast units, when units become damaged during placing. These should be removed from the works and recycled.	Waste (storage and disposal), 3.1.4
Considerable land areas may be required adjacent to the site for the production, curing and storage of pre-cast armour units (ie pre-assembly). Creation of suitably flat temporary areas can have considerable impact on coastal/marine features (eg beaches/dunes). There may also be consequential impacts on wildlife and habitats and there may be associated safety issues.	Wildlife and natural features, 3.6.6
Be aware of potential archaeological discoveries during operations (ie remains and artefacts).	Archaeology and heritage, 3.8.5

4.9   Timber Works

Key issues – Timber works	Refer to
Construction Issues	
Sustainability of materials supply: there are significant certification issues associated with obtaining sustainable tropical hardwoods. Where possible timber should be obtained from suppliers committed to sustainable forest supplies, and moving towards certification.	Guidance published by relevant environment agency
Use of recycled timber should be considered, even if there is a cost premium. Timber will require careful inspection before re-use to identify the depth of any surface deterioration and in many cases may require re-machining and/or appropriate strength grading.	
Old timber waste should be disposed of carefully and only if it cannot be re-used or recycled.	Waste (storage and disposal), 3.1.4 Demolition, 4.1

4.10 Piling

Key issues – Timber works	Refer to
Wastes and emissions from treatment and preservatives. Saw dust and planings from some hardwoods can be hazardous to health. Any working of the timber should be carried out behind screens to contain any wind blown dusts from the public.	Waste (storage and disposal), 3.1.4 Dust, emissions and odours, 3.3.3
Personnel working with the timbers should be adequately advised of the potential hazards and the required personal protection equipment should be worn. Any treatments/preservatives applied on site should be used only in a designated area with suitable protection to avoid pollution of the sea and adjacent habitats.	
The installation of timber piles, groynes etc involves tidal working and associated noise at anti-social hours. However, if driving of piles is required, then consideration should be given to driving only on the day shift or using a muffled hammer or vibro-piling rig. Where possible, working of the timber with chainsaws and/or planers should be carried out in a designated area behind screens. This may not be possible for final installation, but noise near low water may be screened naturally by coastal features.	Noise and vibration, 3.2.4 Piling, 4.10

4.10 Piling

There are two options generally to install piles in a marine environment (ie floating or fixed platform). The floating scenario is restricted and is not suitable for:

1. Drilled piles except in very calm conditions.

2. Raking piles except in very calm conditions.

3. Works that require the ability to resist torque.

4. Works close to navigational channels.

Use of a fixed platform involves either working "hand over hand", using a jack up barge or temporary causeway to get above wave and tidal action. For use of floating plant see Section 4.16 below.

Planning/design issues that may need to be considered prior to commencement of construction work include:

- the merits of steel versus timber piling

- when piling over water, whether to use a floating or fixed platform

- sealing piles.

Key issues – Piling	Refer to

Contractual Conditions

Check your contract and consent documents (as appropriate). What working conditions have been established for activities, if any? If you are uncertain or if a particular issue has not been covered, contact client and/or the relevant authority.

In the majority of cases, piling is likely to be the noisiest activity undertaken on the construction site. As such, it has probably been subject to rigorous pre-construction investigations, with resulting contract conditions in place. Check your contract and the planning conditions to see what restrictions have been imposed upon piling activities. This is particularly important in identified sensitive areas.	Noise and vibration, 3.2.4

Construction Issues

For bored piling/rock socketing, removal of waste ("spoil") and flushings is the major environmental consideration with this work.	Waste (storage and disposal), 3.1.4
In-situ concrete piles will require the same considerations as set out for other in-situ concrete structures in item 4.14 below.	Concrete pours and aftercare, 4.14
Use of "silent" piling should be considered to avoid fish kill, when piling over water. Vibro-piling is often used for timber groyne piles, but heavier hammers may be required for jetty works. It must be appreciated that muffled or silenced piling hammers tend to have a reduced driving efficiency and this may lead to a larger hammer being required.	Shellfish and fish, 3.7.4 Noise and vibration, 3.2.4
Seek advice on the paint to be used, if applicable, to ensure that ingredients are non-hazardous to marine life.	Painting, 4.12 Wildlife and natural features, 3.6.7
Be aware of potential archaeological discoveries during piling activities (ie remains and artefacts).	Archaeology and heritage, 3.8.5

(4.11) Masonry

4.11 Masonry

Very little brand new masonry work is carried out today but masonry structures on the coast are frequently the subject of repairs.

Key issues – Masonry	Refer to
Construction Issues	
Environmental placing issues are similar to those for rock and pre-cast concrete structures	Rock works and placing of concrete units, 4.8
Repairs may involve;	
● repointing	Grouting, 4.13
● drilling and grouting of entire structure	Concrete pours and aftercare, 4.14
● ground and rock anchors, suitably grouted in place	
● support of toe of structure, which may involve grout bags, tremie concrete, grouted aggregate, underwater concrete, rock armour protection	Rock works and placement of concrete units, 4.8
● sprayed concrete.	
To avoid waste from grout loss arising when grouting masonry structures it is essential to ensure that:	Water quality, 3.5.4 Waste (storage and disposal), 3.1.4
● all joints are adequately sealed and pointed prior to grouting (divers will be required to caulk open joints underwater prior to grouting operations)	Dust, emissions and odours, 3.3.3
● grouting is commenced at relatively low pressures to avoid blowing joints	

4.12   Painting

Key issues – Painting	Refer to
Construction Issues	
Dust and emissions: during surface preparation, it is essential to make proper provision for recovery of old paint flakes during shot blasting.	Dust, emissions and odours, 3.3.3
Surface preparation should be carried out in a controlled manner, under sheeted enclosures, which allows the material removed to be adequately collected and disposed of.	
Material removed should be checked for contaminants and dealt with as Special Waste if necessary.	
Shot blasting noise and dust: the shot blasting operation should be carried out behind screens to prevent excess noise and dust emissions, there may be a need to consider water sprays to keep the dust contained.	Noise and vibration, 3.2.4 Dust, emissions and odours, 3.3.3
Health impacts of paint fumes etc: personnel involved in the paint operation should be suitably competent and trained and should be provided with the correct personal protective equipment (PPE), usually breathing apparatus, for the work in hand. In terms of protection for the public the operation should be screened and there may be a need to consider exhaust ventilation.	Dust, emissions and odours, 3.3.3

Grouting and tremie concreting

4.13 Grouting and "tremie" concreting

Key issues – Grouting	Refer to
Construction Issues	
General – follow guidance as for land-based operations.	CIRIA C502, Section 4.10
Carry out disposal of waste additives with care, especially in the case of underwater concrete. The additives in underwater concrete tend to be the plasticisers, introduced during the batching of the mix. However, there are instances where the plasticiser requires addition immediately prior to placing (ie on-site) and care should be taken with the handling and disposal of this material and its containers.	Waste (storage and disposal), 3.1.4
Locate the grout batching area where it will cause least noise disturbance to neighbours.	Noise and vibration, 3.2.4 Water quality 3.5.4
Inevitably, there will need to be a cleaning operation to remove silt or debris to prepare the bed or bottom of a cofferdam, pile etc, to receive grout or tremie concrete. The discharge from the dredging or airlifting operation needs to be controlled so as not to adversely affect water quality.	
Marine grouting is often low pressure and not as susceptible to blow backs and associated dust etc. If grouting is high pressure, follow the recommendations for land-based grouting. When tremie concreting, maintain the outlet below the surface of the concrete to avoid localised wash out.	CIRIA C502, Section 4.10
Discharge of excess grout into water and unnecessary waste etc should be avoided as far as possible when grouting joints and gaps in existing structures (eg masonry).	Masonry, 4.11

Concrete pours and aftercare 4.14

4.14 Concrete pours and aftercare

Key issues – Concrete pours and care	Refer to
Construction Issues	
Follow recommendations in *Environmental good practice on site*.	CIRIA C502, Section 4.5
As discussed in the C502, shutter failure can cause pollution of water bodies. However, when ensuring stability of framework prior to filling with concrete, it is essential that it is designed to accommodate the predicted loadings from wave, current and wind action, particularly when empty.	Water quality, 3.5.4 Dust, emissions and odours, 3.3.3
When concrete is placed in the inter-tidal zone, there is a significantly increased risk of washout of cement, additives and fines when it comes into contact with sea water. Apart from being undesirable structurally, the washout can have undesirable effects on water quality and ecology.	Water quality, 3.5.4 Wildlife and natural features, 3.6.7 Shellfish and fish, 3.7.4
Time concrete pours to provide maximum cure time before the pour is in contact with sea water. Alternatively, look at the use of rapid hardener additives in the mix to promote an early set of the upper surface.	
Use of shutter oils needs to be controlled as recommended in the land-based guide.	CIRIA C502, Section 4.5
However, even with best control, there is still the potential that these oils can get into the water and affect water quality and ecology. Hence, use oils that are biodegradable and environmentally friendly.	Water quality, 3.5.4 Wildlife and natural Shellfish and fish, 3.7.4
During concrete pours there can be considerable noise generated from vibrators, this should be addressed using screens and/or muffled equipment.	Noise and vibration, 3.2.4
Surplus concrete should be stockpiled, recycled and reused by crushing and screening.	
Underwater Concreting.	Issues discussed in Section 4.13

4.15 Asphalt works

Key issues – Asphalt works	Refer to
Construction Issues	
Asphalt production: asphalt will generally be produced off-site and imported. However, when using mastic grout, an imported "half-product" may be upgraded with the addition of bitumen in a mixing unit. The mixing unit issues to be addressed are: energy use, noise, fumes and the potential for bitumen/diesel spills.	Waste (storage and disposal), 3.1.4 Noise and vibration, 3.2.4 Dust, emissions and odours, 3.3.3
Transport to site: imported materials will generally be delivered by road, affecting local communities. Liaise with locals/client/suppliers to define most appropriate delivery routes/times.	Noise and vibration, 3.2.4 Dust, emissions and odours, 3.3.3
Site plant: tidal working leads to noise and emissions outside regular hours. Reduce transport distances if possible. Shield plant behind embankments rather than on their crests.	Noise and vibration, 3.2.4
Installation: there is a risk of diesel/hydraulic spills from plant so try to locate away from water or utilise appropriate preventative measures. A strong odour is associated with asphalt workings so locate away and downwind from residences if possible.	Dust, emissions and odours, 3.3.3
Water quality: asphalt is insoluble and no pollution from leachates will occur. Super penetration primer is used for construction joints in open stone asphalt – this is solvent based so care must be taken to ensure it is not spilled. Note that where used, it should "break" (solvents evaporate) before water comes into contact with it.	Water quality, 3.5.4
Waste materials: asphalt is delivered hot and becomes unusable if it falls below a certain Temperature. Some waste material will result. Minimise waste by using heated, covered delivery bays, shorter site transport routes and by planning ahead (ie weather, tides). Contingency plans for breakdowns should be utilised.	Waste (storage and disposal), 3.1.4
Dealing with waste: open stone asphalt and lean sand asphalt should be collected and returned to supplier, or used as fill. Mastic grout should be re-cycled on-site. Once collected when cooled it can be added to hot boiler and re-used.	Waste (storage and disposal), 3.1.4

4.16   Marine vessels and plant, including maintenance

The main categories of marine plant used include:

- **Tugs** – Specialised push/pull vessels of various sizes. A common factor to nearly all tugs is that they are deep hulled for their size, and often require more draft than the equipment they are moving.

- **Barges** (flat-topped tug pulled, bottom dumping, side tipping) – Generally boat shaped and the majority require a tug to move them around. Towed equipment needs more sea room than self-propelled vessels, particularly under windy conditions, and may be draught-limited by their tug.

- **Pontoons** – Basically a floating steel box, some being fitted with "spuds" and others with winches to anchor them in position. Problems have occurred in the past with pontoons and barges when they are trying to ride out bad weather and their anchoring system fails.

- **Laybarges** – For pipes/cables.

- **Amphibious plant** – Generally designed for the military initially and have the ability to beach themselves, due to their shallow draft, and offload via an in-built ramp.

- **Jack-up barges** – Are pontoons fitted with legs and lifting gear which bears on the sea bed and allows the pontoon to be lifted above the water level to work. They are most vulnerable when manoeuvring and jacking up as they are reliant on tugs or anchors to move and it is not possible to confirm the condition of the seabed.

- **Floating cranes** – Floating cranes can range from land-based crawler cranes being located and secured on a pontoon, to custom-built vessels with large capacity shear legs.

- **Dredgers** (Section 4.2) – Used to excavate the sea bed and either pumping the material ashore or dumping at sea. Their hulls are generally designed as ocean going vessels and can operate in harbours or open sea, they generally require plenty of water under their keels.

Marine vessels and plant, including maintenance

Key issues – Marine vessels and plant	Refer to
Construction Issues	
When refuelling vessels at sea, take great care to avoid spillages due to the relative movements of the vessels. Contingency plans should be considered to contain any spillage on the vessel for subsequent removal to shore when possible.	Water quality, 3.5.4 Wildlife and natural features, 3.6.7 Shellfish and fish, 3.7.4
Take care when the hose is returned after bunkering to avoid any surplus fuel left in the hose discharging directly into the water.	
Take care, when operating with marine plant, to avoid collisions and any consequent emissions of oil, fuel etc, which might have significant impacts on wildlife, habitats, and fisheries. Site all fuel tanks securely and safely so that there is no chance of damage during any vessel impact or collision, leading to discharge of oil or diesel into the sea.	Wildlife and natural features, 3.6.7 Shellfish and fish, 3.7.4 Dust, emissions and odours, 3.3.3
Navigation control zones (arising from mooring ropes and cables) – when using marine equipment relying on anchors for stability and security, the area around the equipment can be severely affected by anchor wires and ropes. For example, when a pontoon has anchor wires 100 to 150 metres out from its four corners, a large area can become inaccessible and navigating vessels will have to be made aware. This may impact on fishing activities and on navigation especially when operating close to navigational channels.	Shellfish and fish, 3.7.4 Wildlife and natural features, 3.6.7
Issues with transhipment of rock.	Rock works, 4.8
Regularly maintain and service all marine plant to avoid oil and/or fuel leaks into the water. Use biodegradable oils where possible to mitigate the impact of any spillage or leakage.	Wildlife and natural features, 3.6.7 Shellfish and fish, 3.7.4
Note that maintenance and service periods represent a time of increased risk for incidents and spills. Ensure protective measures are in place, as appropriate.	Dust, emissions and odours, 3.3.3

Land based plant, including maintenance

4.17 Land based plant, including maintenance

The following kinds of land-based plant, sometimes with modifications (eg excavators), are considered suitable for work in wet/intertidal conditions.

- **Crawler Crane** – The size of the crawler crane will be dictated by the weight of the largest piece of rock armour plus the grab and the radius it is to work at. The travelling speed of crawler cranes restricts how far into the tidal zone they can operate effectively.

- **Hydraulic Excavator** – The size of the excavator will be determined by the size of the material to be placed, the radius is not generally a problem as the machine can track closer to the work front. The travel speed of the excavator makes it more versatile in the tidal zone as it can retreat faster than a crane. Modifications can be made to standard machines to increase boom length and/or insert a turret between tracks and cab to allow working in a depth of water.

- **Steel bodied Dump Trucks** – Used in various sizes to transport rock or fill materials around the site, being very fast and versatile. They are generally filled by hydraulic excavator. Steel bodies are essential to handle rock.

- **Wheeled Loaders** – Depending on the size of rock, and the distance it has to be transported, the wheeled loader can be more effective than a combination of excavator and dump trucks. They have proved themselves very effective in the offloading of rock delivery barges due to the limited space available for manoeuvring on deck.

Checklist – Action in the event of an oil/diesel spillage
Spillage over land:
1:     Report any spillage immediately to the relevant environment agency.
2   Spillage on coastal land/beach – area of spillage to be contained using sand or spill kits.
3   Spilt material to be absorbed using granules or wipes from spill kit; and
4   Materials for clean up to be disposed of in a polythene bag which should be taken to a licensed tip.
Spillage over water:
5   Report any spillage immediately to the maritime and coastguard agency and the relevant environment agency.
6   Area of spill to be contained using floating booms.

4.17 # Land based plant, including maintenance

Key issues – Land based plant	Refer to
Construction Issues	
Follow best practice for land-based plant provided in *Environmental good practice on site*.	CIRIA C502, Section 4.13.
Regularly maintain and service all land based plant to avoid oil and/or fuel leaks into marine/coastal environment. Install drip-trays wherever possible on plant and ensure that they are emptied regularly.	Waste (storage and disposal), 3.1.4 Dust, emissions and odours, 3.3.3
Use biodegradable oils or oil substitutes wherever possible to mitigate the impact of any leakage or accidental spillage of waste oil during oil changes. Develop a protocol for the disposal of wastes from maintenance, including oils which may be deemed to be Special Wastes.	
All fuel should be stored in bunded tanks, with a capacity of tank capacity + 10%. Designate an area for refuelling of vehicles, surface it and bund as surface water run off may be contaminated.	
Beware of tidal and weather conditions on the coast, especially when working within the limits of wave and water action. Secure all plant and equipment during storm conditions to prevent damage to equipment.	Tides and winds, 2.2.2
Oil leaks from machinery: use biodegradable oils wherever possible, ensure machines are well maintained and check hoses and pipework regularly.	Dust, emissions and odours, 3.3.3
Land-based plant and workforce can impact on the natural environment through direct disturbance of habitats and wildlife. Plant and trucks can damage sensitive natural features through crushing of sediment, plants and geological features.	Wildlife and natural features, 3.6.7
If working in a designated sites, take care not to encroach into sensitive areas and keep to selected access lanes and agreed working areas.	